Who Owns
the Earth?

D1234058

TO KNOW   TO UNDERSTAND   TO PARTICIPATE
THE CANADIAN HERITAGE IS YOUR HERITAGE

**ALBERTA HERITAGE
LEARNING RESOURCES
PROJECT**

A Project of Alberta Education
Funded
By
The Alberta Heritage Savings Trust Fund
and
Dedicated to the Students
of Alberta
by the
Government of Alberta
1979

Grateful acknowledgment is extended
to those who assisted in the development
of the Alberta Heritage anthologies

Members of the Selection Committee

Theresa Ford / *Edmonton Catholic School District*
Michael Allen / *Calgary Catholic School District*
Tom Gee / *Alberta Education*
Marg Iveson / *Edmonton Public School District*
Gloria Limin / *Calgary Public School District*
Lorne MacRae / *Calgary Public School District*
Maureen Ross / *Edmonton Catholic School District*

Western Canadian Literature
for Youth

Who Owns
the Earth?

Theresa M. Ford
Managing Editor

Alberta Education
Edmonton

Alberta Education
Devonian Building
11160 Jasper Avenue
Edmonton, Alberta
T5K 0L2

ISBN 0-920794-16-5

Project Director/Dr. Kenneth Nixon
Design/David Shaw & Associates Ltd.
Publishing Consultants/Hurtig Publishers, Edmonton
Illustration/Tibor Kovalik
Typesetting & Printing/Lawson Graphics Western Ltd., Calgary
Binding/Economy Bookbinding Company Ltd., Calgary

To the Reader

"No man is an island!"

We have read these words in poetry, heard them in song, but have we, in reality, subscribed to their message: that we are *all* interdependent?

Our personal survival depends not only upon our fellow human beings but upon Earth's other vivifying entities as well: plant life and animal life. During the last few generations, those resources have been squandered ruthlessly. As a result, we have been forced during this decade to re-evaluate our use — and our misuse — of our fragile environment.

Who owns the earth? At first glance this may seem a very philosophical title for an anthology. In actual fact, the answer to the question is fundamental to our own heritage and crucial to the heritage of those who come after us. We must ensure that the treasures of Earth are responsibly bequeathed to the generations who are yet unborn.

Contents

Who Owns the Earth?

Let Them Eat Sawdust

Roderick Haig-Brown

I have been, all my life, what is known as a conservationist. I am not at all sure that this has done myself or anyone else any good, but I am quite sure that no intelligent man, least of all a country man, has any alternative. It seems clear beyond possibility of argument that any given generation of men can have only a lease, not ownership, of the earth; and one essential term of the lease is that the earth be handed on to the next generation with unimpaired potentialities. This is the conservationist's concern.

It is in the history of civilizations that conservationists are always defeated, boomers always win, and the civilizations always die. I think there has never been, in any state, a conservationist government, because there has never yet been a people with sufficient humility to take conservation seriously. This is natural enough. No man is intimately concerned with more than his lifetime, comparatively few men concern themselves seriously with more than a fraction of that time; in the last analysis all governments reflect the concerns of the people they govern, and most modern democratic governments are more deeply concerned with some brief, set term of office than with anything else. Conservation means fair and honest dealing with the future, usually at some cost to the immediate present. It is a simple morality, with little to offset the glamor and quick material rewards of the North American deity, 'Progress'.

Living near a settlement like Elkhorn on Vancouver Island, one sees both sides of the argument lived out, and inevitably takes part. Elkhorn is entirely dependent on natural resources in their first state. Almost the whole of Vancouver Island is, or was, timber; possibly the finest softwood saw-log timber in the world. Next in importance to timber are the recreational assets — game, game fish, and scenery; after these, commercial fishing, coal mining, agriculture, and water power. Elkhorn is touched by all of them, but timber is overwhelmingly the most important factor in its existence; the whole forty-year life of the village has been built on service to the logging camps and loggers of the surrounding country. And during those years the importance of a tourist trade based mainly on sport fishing has steadily increased.

It would be logical to suppose that everyone in Elkhorn would be interested in forestry and forest conservation, but almost no one is. Vancouver Island's forests were at first considered 'inexhaustible'; then, as it became clear that they were being rapidly exhausted, the forests became an expendable asset, to be used in 'opening up the country' so that some unspecified phenomenon, probably 'industry', could come in and take over. That is where things rest at present. Elkhorn and other little towns like it watch the big logging camps draw farther and farther away as the more accessible timber is cleared off; they know vaguely that the end of saw-log timber is in sight, that millions of deforested acres are reproducing only slowly if at all; yet they retain a mystic faith in the future, a belief that 'progress' in the shape of roads and wharves and airplanes and hydroelectric power will somehow lead them on to continuously more abundant life. Perhaps they will. But even that could not excuse or justify the fire-destroyed acres, the incredible waste of timber in logging, the long barren years through which magnificent forestland has grown little or nothing.

Elkhorn is in no way unique. This frantic dream of progress and development has cursed nearly every hamlet and village in North America at some time or another, bringing with it premature sidewalks and false-front stores, fantastic real-estate projects, fierce neon signs and an orgy of public services planned with a solidity that might better have gone into the jerry-built houses. Usually it is a recurrent frenzy, starting with each sizable economic boom, dying back between whiles to surge up again on some new promise of oil or minerals or large construction, any high and easy road to sudden wealth. And it is not wholly bad. It has built a continent's material civilization, blatantly, wastefully, with an enormous cruelty in the shattering of men's hopes and dreams, and frequent distortions of true values; but it has built it, and perhaps it was necessary to build so fast and so extravagantly.

But now that the continent is crossed and secured the method seems stupid, the haste merely destructive. The sanctity of 'progress' with its tricky little catch phrase, 'We can't stand in the way of progress', seems suddenly false and treacherous. It is a good time to ask, 'Why can't we?', to pull progress apart and take a new look at it, to examine everything called 'development' in terms of values that already exist, in its relationship to the economy of the whole nation and the whole continent; above all, in its relationship to human happiness.

Progress seems to mean, all too often, the projection of slums into the wilderness. Incredibly, for all its village size, Elkhorn achieved slums for itself on land that had been bush only a year previously. This came about in a sudden flux of temporary jobs on a major construction project; people poured in, found high wages, then paid higher rents for tar-paper shacks set in mud, where each family shared a single room and a dozen families shared a hand pump for water, and an outside toilet. The project was finished, many of the families moved out and the village had time to wonder what had happened to it. Meanwhile the timber has drawn back two or three years farther into the mountains. But more people than ever before are dependent on it.

So the more abundant life has arrived briefly and departed, much of it spent in failure and waste. High wages have little meaning if they will buy only tar-paper shacks as transient homes for growing children. Boom and progress and development add up to high real-estate prices, houses scattered among vacant lots that no one can afford to buy, a few short lengths of sidewalk, some no-parking signs, and a multiplicity of stores with little reason to be doing business. And the village settles back to consolidate. Strangely, there is something to consolidate. More people are living in the community, even though there is apparently less reason for them to be doing so. There is a framework of community organization, something beyond the simple mutual help of the older days. There are many improved services, such strange exotic things as street lights and an up-to-date water system and an extremely modern school. Some of these things may prove difficult to maintain and pay for; but they exist and merely by doing so they make a village out of what had been only a settlement. Somehow timber and tourists will support them until another boom comes and a few more of the vacant lots between the houses are filled and a small town begins to grow out of the village. But the solidity, the real existence of the town, as of the village, will be built only slowly, between the booms.

It is difficult to know how much or how little human happiness grows out of such a boom, but the total seems less than before. There are more worried and anxious and uncertain people than there were before. Even small businessmen who have done well are strained by their expansion, working harder, worrying more, remembering the quieter, more logical times with regret. Even the most ambitious of them speak regretfully of simplicities they loved in the earlier Elkhorn, which now seem lost in the surge of progress they called for. Yet they must seem to call for more progress because the deity is sacrosanct; no North American businessman can deny her lip service, no matter what may be in his heart.

A conservationist fights many battles, varying in scale all the way from the attempted protection of some individual species of wildlife to the supreme issue of proper use of soil, air, and water; and every fight is complicated, if not forced, by the false urgency and outdated sanctity of progress. The speed of modern development is such that the conservationist is always under attack, rarely has time himself to attack. He needs only breathing space, a little time for thoughts to creep in and temper progress with wisdom. Development is rarely a matter of urgency. Timber, soil, fisheries, oil and minerals, even water power, become more, not less, valuable with delay. The problem is to use the self-reproducing resources within their safe yield and to develop the wasting resources without injury to others already producing.

Elkhorn, when a government was damming its river, had to fight and fight hard to save the salmon run on which its tourist trade is built. She had to fight again, still harder, to win clearing of the land that would be flooded by the dam. She expects, and needs, a pulp mill; probably it will come one day and if it does she will have to fight again, harder than ever before, to save her waters from pollution.

Such conflicts as these go on throughout the continent, and none of them is necessary. Hydroelectric developments, pulp mills, and other such manifestations of progress are not dreamed up overnight. There is always ample time for mature and careful consideration of every issue involved. But early planning is always left to the single-track minds of the developers, often buried in deepest secrecy for purely commercial reasons, and the conservationist is left with a last-ditch battle. In this way the burden of proof is always forced upon him. He is standing in the way of progress — reactionary, narrow, without real vision.

It seems clear to me that all destruction it causes should be reckoned in the direct cost of any project, and that no preventable destruction should ever be permitted. Obviously flooded land is no longer land in any useful sense; but it should be cleared of timber and debris before flooding so that a lake with good bottom and clean shores will take its place. If the cost of this is too great for the project to bear, then the project is uneconomic. Runs of game and commercial fish can be destroyed by poorly planned dams; but sound planning can always find some way to compensate and may even save the whole resource. The onus here is just as clear, if not clearer, since a run of fish properly looked after will maintain itself indefinitely into the future, while a hydroelectric development may be outdated within twenty years, almost certainly will be within fifty years. Pollution of air and water by industrial plants is the simplest issue of all. There are adequate means of preventing all such pollutions. Admittedly they are sometimes costly, but if the industry cannot support the cost it is economically unsound. No nation can afford polluted air or polluted waterways.

These are sweeping statements, and I mean them to be. A civilization built on foul air and polluted water, on destroyed timber lands, overgrazed ranges, exhausted farm lands, on water sucked from one river system to make cheap electricity on another, is too costly and too insecurely based to last. I saw recently a newspaper editorial happily forecasting that before very long the world's timber supplies will be too valuable for any such simple use as building houses or making paper; they will all be needed for human food — processed, no doubt, into pulpy palatability, but still essentially sawdust. Any civilization that can cheerfully contemplate such a morbid future for its multiplied grandchildren needs a new philosophy.

Industrial development has produced such an enormous material prosperity, so widely spread, that its sanctity is easy to understand. But in North America it has done so largely by using capital assets as income. That is why conservation is now far more important than further development. It seems to me that the people of the continent, both Canadians and Americans, have everything to gain, nothing to lose, by stopping to take stock and understand what they have got and how it can soundly be used. Exhausting a continent and overpopulating it to the point at which its inhabitants must start eating trees seems a strange way to a more abundant life.

It is difficult to believe the theorists who say that a nation to be sound must have an increasing population. Thousands of years ago the human race had to breed tolerably fast to survive. After that nations had to grow large populations in fear of wars. And there was always the idea that man must multiply until he had overrun the earth. He seems to have achieved this and surely he can be allowed to pause to recognize that there is no virtue in population for the sake of population; if there were, India, China, even Russia would be more prosperous nations than they are. It is difficult to believe that there is any true morality in producing children, or any essential immorality in not producing them. Certainly there is little to be said for raising men to be slaves to 'progress' and cities, to industry and all the machines of a civilization frantically producing substitutes for the natural things it has destroyed.

Conservation is wise use of natural resources, which ultimately are the whole life of any country, even one that imports most of its natural resources. And it is axiomatic that no special interest, whether it is industrial or governmental, can be trusted to use raw materials wisely. All resources are interdependent; soil, for instance, cannot be separated from water tables, nor water tables from forests; and all life that moves on the land, in the water, or in the air is affected by every use of these resources. The conservationist's hope — perhaps dream is the better word — is to establish a co-ordination of effort that will make sure that every factor is properly weighed and every resource fully protected against exploitation or wanton destruction.

Perhaps I take too much pleasure in prophesying doom, perhaps I am too much countryman and woodsman to understand the dream of progress through cities and machines, to feel the romance of the bulldozer and the earth mover, the concrete mixer and the four-lane highway. But I think we are on our way through the whole tragic story, that we shall live well on it. Our children and grandchildren and great-grandchildren will have to solve the slow, difficult problem of restoration as best they can. Perhaps atomic power will help them. It seems to be our only legacy.

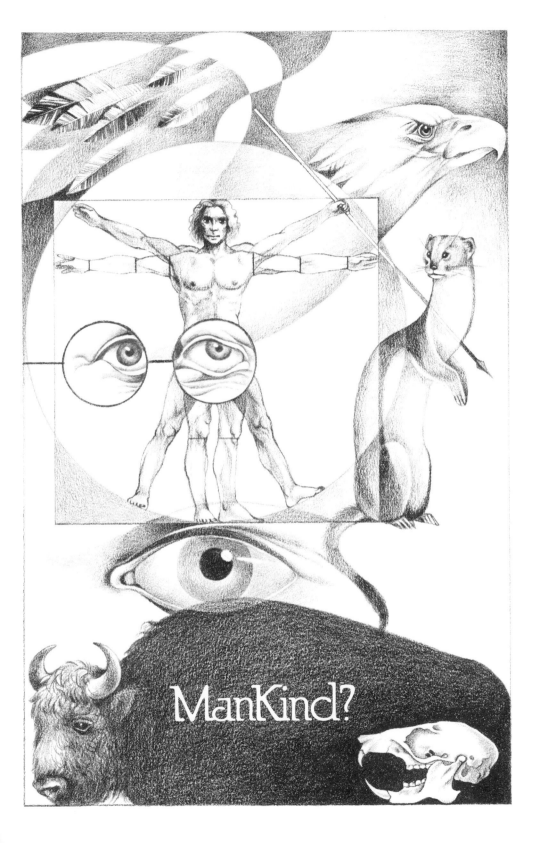

ManKind?

Neither Voice Nor Vote

Convocation Address for May 30, 1972,
University of Alberta

Al Oeming

Mr. Chancellor, Mr. President, honored guests, members of the graduating class, ladies and gentlemen:

Every generation goes forth facing a plethora of problems — wars, recessions, social revolutions and unrest.

But yours is a truly critical generation. For it stands at the very crossroads of all life. The way you treat this earth and its natural life will determine what kind of a world future generations will inherit, if indeed there is anything left to pass on.

With your different backgrounds, hopes and aspirations, and with most of you following your own individual paths, one area of concern will be starkly common to all of you. We all share the same earth. We all have become very much aware of that factor called the environment. We no longer want to breathe our own apathy. My particular concern is the fate of the lesser creatures who also inhabit this earth . . . those creatures who have neither voice nor vote.

Obviously until very recent times man felt he had nothing to gain by peacefully sharing this world with the lower forms of life. A very quick review of what he has done since he made his first extermination of a species, the European lion around 80 A.D., indicates that man's activities have been responsible for exterminating at least three per cent of the world's approximately 4,000 species and subspecies of mammals. Birds fared little better and none of us will ever know how many other life forms such as reptiles, amphibians, plants and lesser organisms have been permanently destroyed.

Only a century ago the American bison roamed the North American plains in millions, providing food, clothing and shelter for the conquering whites as they had always done for the native Indians. The most famous of the herds was so large that instead of estimating its size in numbers it was said to be twenty-five miles long and fifty miles wide. The new coast-to-coast railway ran through the middle of this vast herd dividing it into a southern half and a northern half. In 1877 one hundred thousand of the southern herd were shot and by 1899 the herd was completely annihilated. Fortunately the prairie bison averted extinction and today we and future generations will enjoy them in the safety of national parks and similar zoological institutions.

Other wild creatures were not so fortunate, and man has left a sordid and lengthy testimony of his inhumanity to the lesser creatures. The demise of the Passenger Pigeon is one of the most tragic. Perhaps no other species so well indicates that abundance is no guarantee of survival. Once the commonest bird in America, its numbers were reckoned in the thousands of millions, and individual flocks were said to "darken the sky". One small Michigan town shipped three carloads of pigeons a day for 40 days — about twelve million birds at half a penny each. One man alone, in 1883 in Missouri, killed 60,000 helpless young birds. The last survivor died on September 1, 1914, in the Cincinnati Zoo.

During the night of June 4, 1844, three fishermen sailed to

the Island of Eldey, off the southern tip of Iceland. There they killed the last two Great Auks. The men who perpetrated this deed did commit an evil, more lasting than that of the Greek Herostratus who set fire to the Temple of Ephesus so that his name should not be forgotten. Both before and since, men have built and destroyed Temples, but all of mankind together cannot recreate a species. We can build immense skyscrapers, destroy whole continents with nuclear weapons, but to bring a dead worm back to life is beyond us.

The threat to wild animals is still with us, and it is accelerating. Over 50 per cent of the known species losses have occurred since 1900. We have obviously learned little from the dark past.

"Well, there's room in this world for all of us," says Mr. Average Man, sitting in his rumpus room and ruminating over such matters. But what a fateful and mendacious catch-phrase that is. . . .

In our gigantic cities, we live beneath blankets of dirty grey miasma, which dim the light of the sun, smart the nostrils and burn the eyes. Our industrial centres suck up the basic water from the land, and then pollute the rivers with the vile effluents which they discharge. But men have not always been so insensitive to the wild creatures about them.

Near Lascaux, France, and Altamira, Spain, are found the oldest paintings in the world. Artists living some 25,000 years ago covered the walls and ceilings of caves with images of horses, bison and red deer. Surely men who expended such great effort, working from terribly cramped postures, were awed and impressed by the beauty of the animals they painted.

Is it that man, prior to the invention of Agriculture, so desperately depended upon wild animals for food, clothing and shelter? He was a hunter. He had to know a great deal about the animals he sought, for it meant the difference between life and death. Early man may well have formed his first means of spoken communication between such hunting parties. In fact, early man's interest in wild animals became a life-long research that may have become part of our genetic composition.

World literature is replete with references to animals. The Greek poet Homer, in the *Iliad,* draws parallels between the history of wildlife and the drama of the Trojan war. Melville's *Moby Dick,* Coleridge's *Rime of the Ancient Mariner* could hardly have been written without the existence of the animals they described.

The first Zoological Garden of which we have information was founded in China by the first Emperor of the Chou Dynasty, who reigned about 1100 B.C. It was called ''The Intelligence Park'', and had both a scientific and an educational objective.

We could, then, be undermining our cultural and behavioural foundation if we continue to lose wild creatures at the present rate. What is the biological significance of this loss? What would be the effect on the general well-being of this world if we lose the Whooping Crane, the Polar Bear and the Bald Eagle?

It would seem absurd for a passenger in some hypothetical future space ship to discard life-support equipment because he did not understand its function or significance, and he wanted the extra space for more comfortable accommodations. Yet, there is a clear analogy between this example and today's problem of threatened wildlife. We know so little about the ecology of the earth that we are not yet in a position to define the role of most living species, and, thus, to evaluate their significance to our own life-support system. Extermination of a species today means much more than a tomorrow with fewer species.

What do we really feel when we thrill to the sight of a majestic Wood Bison in the last reddish glow of a northern sunset, or the careless expenditure of enormous muscular power in the rough play of a couple of Siberian Tigers?

Civilization has evidently not destroyed this inherited

interest in wildlife. We have, however, displayed an insensitivity to the delicacy of the ecological balance, and far too often based our actions on a materialistic greed. But the basic fascination is still with us. How else can you explain the world-wide publicity that animal exchanges receive? The Muskox and Giant Panda exchange between the United States and China was a notable example. Animals still appear to be the ideal good-will Ambassadors between nations of differing ideologies. No one as yet has laid claim to their having been indoctrinated!

In this crowded, polluted and artificial world, man needs periodically to get away from the rat race, and commune with nature. The howling of wolves on a cold moonlit night in our northern forests, long skeins of waterfowl on migration flights — these help us retain our sanity and divert us from the pressures of the modern world.

As well, our scientific knowledge benefits from our use of many species of wildlife. Laboratory experiments using animals are conducted every day in the hope that we may eventually conquer all of man's diseases. The first space travellers were animals. Detailed behavioural studies today are being made with primates, which in turn will help us to better understand the psychology of man.

We have long recognized the biological similarities between man and animals. And yet this truth tends to be obscured when we think of ourselves as strange independent creatures living in our cities.

But not only are wild creatures threatened with extinction — mankind is threatened too. The combination of a technological society and a human population that increases by 600,000 people every three and one half days has allowed man to alter his environment drastically in a few short years. If we continue to increase our population with no checks, and further reduce the capacity of the environment to absorb the waste products, then the changes we inflict upon our environment are irreversible. Eventually we reach a point of no return . . . extinction is inevitable. Many ecologists believe that we have already gone too far. They cite the presence of chemicals such as DDT in all species; the horrendous increase in carbon dioxide from the burning of fossil fuels. Captain Jacques Cousteau has stated that the oceans of the world are dying. All of this is irreversible.

Is man then to be added to the ever-growing list of species headed for extinction? Is there a formula for survival? I am optimistic enough to say yes. We can survive, and most other species can also. But man must first realize that the resources of this earth are not infinite. We must impose finite limits on our population and certainly on the exploitation of our natural resources.

Today as never before there is an awakening; an awareness of what must be done, and where we have gone wrong. Small handfuls of dedicated people are winning major victories over giant industrial cartels. Industrial exploiters are afraid to venture against the public outcry that seeks to protect and sustain our natural environment. Industry is cooperating, and I do feel that for the first time in our history, there will be a working together of all interests. In this lies the real hope. Our technological skills are such that we can re-cycle our waste accumulations, and restore polluted rivers to their original life-supporting freshness. The River Thames is a shining example of what man can do.

All my life I have been intensely interested in animals. Having today so many hundreds in my care, I am encouraged by the genuine concern and affection that people from every walk of life show towards them. The Graduates of today must lead the way. You are the vanguard! You must fight the battle against misuse of our natural environment. Love and respect for living creatures flows from love and respect for the highest qualities and aspirations of mankind. All who see the need to save the natural areas of the world and the wildlife of the world *must* work together. Then there is every hope that future generations will go on seeing and being inspired by the Polar Bear, the Rhinoceros, the Elephant, the shy Gorilla — forever.

A Tour of the Alberta Game Farm with Al Oeming

Theresa Ford

Do you love animals — tame, wild, big or small? So do I! As a result of this life-long interest, I have been a frequent visitor at the Alberta Game Farm, a 1,400-acre preserve for endangered species, located 14 miles east of Edmonton.

One visit there, on a crisp October morning, will stand out in my memory as something special. On that day, Dr. Al Oeming, the founder and owner of the Game Farm, gave me a personal tour of his dream-come-true. I would like to share this tour with you in the hope that, in your own way, you will do whatever *you* can, to conserve endangered species.

Dr. Oeming's dream originated when he was still a very young boy. He remembers, "As much as I read about wild animals and as much as I could learn in the field, I had an all-abiding desire to *do* something for them. I had a very strong urge to keep animals on my own, to give them spacious areas for living, to take in animals that I knew were doing poorly in the wild because of loss of habitat, persecution by man and other factors that were detrimental to their survival as a living species. I wanted very much to have my own domain. I felt that I had a rapport with wild animals and I wanted to enhance this association. It was then that I began to wonder how and if ever, I might bring this about, for I realized it would be a very expensive undertaking. I simply didn't *have* the money or the financial connections.

"When World War II was declared I enlisted in the Navy and travelled to Australia, New Zealand, the Fiji Islands and covered quite an amount of the Pacific Archipelago.

"I was fortunate to survive the war years and return home, enriched by the experience and knowledge I had gained.

"I had put my time in the service to good use. I had always followed a program of very active physical recreation. I did a steady routine of exercises which included weights, calisthenics and high-bar work. To enjoy the outdoor world I had to be in superb physical condition — be able to walk many miles a day, climb mountains and trees. I never smoked and seldom had a drink. I just loved feeling 100 per cent fit.

"I had enough Naval time to grant me three years' free tuition at the university of my choice. I enrolled in the zoology department of the University of Alberta. This department was headed by the famous Dr. William Rowan, my long-time friend and mentor.

"As a single veteran student, I received from the Federal Government a $60 monthly allowance — hardly enough to start saving towards a Game Farm! There simply *had* to be a ship of good fortune looming my way on a distant horizon if I was ever to fulfil my dream!

"While in the Navy I had been a close friend and companion of an outstanding Canadian wrestler, Stu Hart. He had indicated that when he left the Naval service, he would join a professional wrestling circuit in the New England states, New York and Boston. If he did well, he promised, he would let me know in case I wanted to join him. Hart was a superb amateur wrestler and had coached me for some time. I wasn't any world beater as an amateur and didn't expect to be one as a professional but the kind of money wrestling could bring to help me achieve my dream of a game reserve, was very enticing.

"After my first year at university, I joined Stu in April and made relatively good money during the summer. But I was wondering how I could justify five months' absence for a professional wrestling tour to my university professor who expected *some* participation in the zoology field during the summer months. You might say that it was all in the aid of wildlife, but it was very difficult to convince my professor!

"However, I carried on and after two summers in wrestling competition, turned to promotion of the sport. The Sales Pavilion on the fair grounds in Edmonton was under construction and was to seat 3,200 people in amphitheatre style.

Perfect for wrestling! With Stu Hart wrestling and me promoting, we formed a partnership that I hoped would restore professional wrestling to Edmonton and provide me with the necessary bank account to buy land and animals.

"Those first hopes were thin, the initial crowd was something under a hundred people. Hart and I were shelling out our reserve money to pay the talent, the rent, travel and advertising costs.

"The second week wasn't any better and the third week was perilous because an even higher-priced performer was coming in. Al 'Mr. Murder' Mills would be featured in the main event against Pat 'Irish' McGill. Mills was a villain, McGill a baby face, who had adoring fans everywhere. I had dished out a lot of complimentary tickets, filling the house until there were about a thousand people there, so that it didn't look too bad.

"Then disaster struck! A concessionaire's error turned the wrestling match into a donnybrook. Instead of selling soft drinks in paper cups, he let everyone take the *bottles* of pop to their seats!

"The main event between Mills and McGill was a hot affair; in fact it generated such heat that the fans went out of control and for twenty minutes they rained pop bottles on the ring. The recently retired Chief of Police was the time keeper and as he rose to strike the gong a ginger ale bottle hit him on the head — and floored him! I can still see the Chief, who reminded me of an aging but powerful bull dog, rising to his feet shouting, 'I'll don a uniform if this persists!'

"The police were powerless to stop the melee and after half an hour the floor was four inches deep in broken glass. Finally the city police riot squad restored some sense of order. I was certain my dreams of a reserve for endangered wildlife lay crushed on the floor with the shattered pop bottles.

"An official investigation was ordered by the mayor and I had to appear before all sorts of civic boards pleading my cause. McGill gave me an enormous amount of help. He was a compelling speaker and very articulate. He begged the governing bodies to please allow him one more chance; it was after all, a concessionaire's error and he wanted one more chance to avenge himself on Al 'Mr. Murder' Mills.

"The permission for a re-match signalled the onset of ten solid years of professional wrestling in Edmonton. The business was good to me, for it allowed me the time to pursue my wildlife studies and I quietly and steadily built up the capital I needed to start on my life's ambition.

"In 1957 I was finally able to purchase the first 500 acres of this land which includes beautiful one-and-a-half-mile-long Lost Lake. The first wild animal exhibits were settled in their new home in 1958, and on August 1, 1959, the Alberta Game Farm was opened to the public. Since then an additional 900 acres have been added. Now, are you ready for the tour?"

Al picked up a pail of stale dinner rolls to attract his animals and we were off . . .

Just inside the gates we stopped to visit two unusual playmates, Hector, a 500-pound Bengal tiger, and Satan, a 20-pound black dog. For four years, the two animals have lived and played together.

"We did not want to put the Bengal in with the Siberian tigers, but Hector was lonely so we went to the pound and picked up this little mongrel."

"And who is the *boss* here?" I asked.

"Why Satan, of course!"

We spent at least half an hour inside the enclosure with the lumbering but friendly one-humped dromedaries. The original sire of these camels was Aly. Rita, his first mate, is now becoming quite frail and will soon be taken to the barn and pampered for her remaining years. Since 1960, she has presented the Game Farm with fifteen baby camels. Because of the rigors of their original environment, camels only deliver one offspring at a time. Twins would be too much to handle in the desert!

Aly, however, no longer associates with the herd because he was deposed by one of his sons. All herd animals have a king with a crown prince waiting in the wings. As old age caught up with Aly, his younger, more vigorous son took over leadership of the herd. Aly was then given his own paddock with a fence separating him from his former kingdom. The keepers noticed that he was beginning to pine away, obviously from a broken heart and sense of loss. Something had to be done! The solution was to move Humper, a bottle-raised two-humped camel, in with Aly. Now the deposed king had someone to boss around again — and a reason to keep on living!

If you visit Aly when he isn't eating — which he is doing most of the time — notice how his lower lip hangs down. Camels inflate their tongues to cause the lower lip to sag when they wish to gain attention and show off. It is their way of saying, "You may not realize it, but I am a *very* important member of this camel society!"

Later, in the paddock of Bactrian or double-humped camels, we met Jasmine, the first Bactrian camel to be born in Canada. She is a prima donna and she knows it. All you have to do is look at the way she makes *her* bottom lip droop!

Grazing with the camels are many llamas. Al informed me these are really cameloids belonging to the same family as the camels. They are, however, a New World animal and are not native to the near or far east.

We spent some time with the delicately beautiful Formosa sika deer. The herd numbers about forty — probably more than on the entire Island of Formosa.

Then to the Siberian tigers.

"We negotiate with Russia for tigers in exchange for cougars and muskox. These are pure Siberians, duly registered. This is a new breeding pen for Bruno who is old enough to mate now. The three females are Sasha, Simmla, and Sirene. Because their mother would have nothing to do with them, we hand-raised the females with a bottle."

The three came over to the fence to have noses and ears scratched. The imperious Bruno, however, kept his distance!

We were walking between the two fences and continued to

the next breeding enclosure where Robo, a magnificent 730-pound Siberian, holds court for four females and a year-old kitten.

Al explained, "Tigers really don't *roar* the way lions do. When they make a snorting noise it is called *chuffling*. When they meow, it is called *tittling*. But they just don't have a roar."

At this point, the mother of the kitten appeared in front of us. In my best 'I'd love to be your friend' tone of voice, I bent towards her and said "Oh, you've come to visit, have you?" In a flash she leaped to her hind feet so that her face was immediately opposite mine, opened her immense jaws with those incredibly long flesh-tearing fangs and let out a terrifying roar as she clawed in my direction with her huge paws.

I leaped backward into the brush, then when I realized there still was a fence between us, I turned to Al and insisted "Now *don't* tell me that was a chuffle or a tittle, Dr. Oeming, *that* was a *roar*!" Al laughed it off with, "Well, that's as much of a roar as a tiger has."

"And *that* is enough for me!"

As Al explained, we were on *her* territory and that was *her* kitten, so by mutual consent we all parted company.

The Snow leopard's enclosure is empty now, for the pair who occupied it surpassed all longevity records for their species before dying at the age of twenty-seven. In May 1964, they produced two kittens and raised them without any outside assistance — a remarkable event, indeed, for there have been very few instances of successful breeding of Snow leopards. This pair of kittens was sent to the zoo in Omaha, Nebraska.

"Here are the Père David's deer which have proved to be exceptionally hardy here at the Alberta Game Farm. There are only about 400 of these deer alive in the world today. During the Boxer Rebellion in China a few were rescued and sent to the Duke of Bedford's estate in England, and all those surviving today have been reintroduced into their native China by shipments from England.

"The Chinese call the Père David deer 'milu', meaning 'the deer of the five unlikes'. It has the tail of the donkey, the feet of the caribou, the unorthodox growth of antlers in bunches with no specific shape, the change in coat colour three times a year, and oriental almond-shaped eyes different from any other species of deer."

Like most visitors to the Game Farm, Al and I spent a long time watching the gorillas cavorting in their compound. At first, Sultan, the big male mountain gorilla was out of sight but Al kept calling, "C'mon, Sultan, you old rogue, come up and see us!" and rattling the pail of dried bread rolls. Soon Sultan strolled up and looked around to see where 'his master's voice' was coming from and contentedly munched on a roll.

Sultan and Zakula, the female, are mountain gorillas from Zaire while the smaller Carlos is a lowland male. Sultan's back is beginning to take on the magnificent silver tones of the adult male even though he is only seven years old now and will continue to grow until he is fourteen.

"They all enjoy fresh cow's milk which they drink out of styrofoam cups. They never crush the cups but politely hand them back for refills.

"Carlos is a real scamp! He is very friendly and will snuggle up to hug and kiss you. But the next thing you know, he has your wrist watch. He'll hold it up to his ear, listen for a bit — then pitch it!"

Although I realized the question had probably been asked many times before, I simply *had* to ask what had been the most frightening experience Dr. Oeming had ever had with a wild animal.

Without a second's delay, he answered, "It happened right here on the farm. During the winter the rhinos sleep inside their barn. Gubetuga, the female white rhino, had become quite tame. However, she must have been sleeping very deeply when I went into the barn on this particular day. I patted her on the rear end and in much less time than you can imagine, 8,000 pounds of rhino leaped to her feet and with that powerful horn pressed against my abdomen, she pinned me against the wall! You know how people say that when death seems imminent, their entire life flashes before them? Well, it's true. All I could think of was, that in one moment of stupidity, I was kissing it all good-bye! However, in the calmest voice I could muster, I kept saying 'It's O.K., Guby, it's just me, Guby, I'm not going to hurt you, Guby.' Miraculously, Gubetuga inched back, I ducked under her belly and ran out the door. Boy, did I run out that door!''

The white rhinoceros is the largest of the five extant races of rhino. Unfortunately all five are becoming extremely rare. Dr. Oeming recalls the expedition to the Umfolozi White Rhino Preserve in Natal, South Africa.

"In 1964 I applied to the Conservation Department of the Government of South Africa for permission to bring back two live white rhinos to Canada. Under the protection of the government, this second largest land mammal in the world was making a come-back from near extinction. Since there is only so much room for a beast even in this large unfenced National Park, when the rhinos become surplus to their food supply they spread out onto the surrounding farms. A rhino that can weigh up to ten thousand pounds can do a great deal of damage tramping down crops of maize and other farm crops so desperately needed by the people of that country.

"So, to alleviate this problem, it was now possible to buy the rhinos for approximately $12,000 a pair. The cost had to be paid in advance. Then the animals could be collected with the assistance of very competent Game Department personnel, and at the buyer's expense, transported to Canada by freighter. In every way *I* had to rustle up the dollars. Fortunately, I had a very successful series of lecture and film shows in Vancouver and so raised the necessary funds.

"April in South Africa is a glorious time of year. The

weather was beautiful, the scenery superb and the excellent Zulu assistants — sixty of them — were matchless in their ability and their strength in assisting with the heavy crates for the rhinos.

"We named the male Thombathini, meaning rough timbers, because he kept breaking the timbers of the crates. When the female was being captured, the tranquilizer missed and the rhino crashed into the thornicaceous trees where she lay in wait for the silver-helmeted Zulu on horseback who was an essential member of the team. Believe me, there were others who took refuge in the bushes! And so we named her Gubetuga, 'bushes where the warriors hid'.

"Once the rhinos were crated and allowed to settle down a bit and once we were confident that they would feed in the crates, the job of transporting them to Durban, the point of embarkation, got under way.

"For this purpose I had earlier secured the service of two East Indian drivers with their trucks. The trucks were rather desperate-looking affairs but both Anthony and Richard, the drivers, assured me with the most solemn promises that the trucks were road-worthy and would make it.

"It was a torturous journey! How many flat tires and boiled-over radiators we had, I couldn't tell you but the whole rigorous trip was lightened by John Jamieson, an amateur photographer, but above all a comedian and a magician. He kept us laughing all the way.

"We arrived finally in the Port of Durban where the crated rhinos were hoisted on board the Norwegian freighter S.S. *Thorshope* and placed on deck where they would travel. We had to use alfalfa, or lucerne as it was called there, a long grassy hay, both for bedding and feed since they had no straw bedding. I had stocked up on a number of ordinary baby's plastic bath tubs. We used these for watering the animals and slid them under the lower bar of the front of the crates.

"The ocean voyage was truly enjoyable and though they

were a little seasick at times, the rhinos behaved well. Every morning and evening the cruise passengers made their pilgrimage down to see Thumbothini and Gubetuga. The rhinos had by this time tamed down considerably and were eating well, although the male was a fussy eater. At the least little untoward movement, or if the water pans were pushed in a bit too far, the baby bathtub would immediately be punctured by that huge sharp horn which, in spite of his bulk, he used with lightning speed. But when I spoke gently to him and if I had time to get things done before people cluttered around, there was never a problem.

"Finally we arrived at the Port of Montreal. Here the real trouble started! The rhinos were slung by huge winches off the ship — one into the box of the truck and one into the trailer. Just as this was done, a rather officious-looking Federal Government veterinarian came up. He examined the import documents. Everything required by the Canadian Government had been adhered to by the officials in South Africa, and I thought we were safe to proceed. But he turned to me and said, 'I want those rhinos placed in water-proofed crates!' Can you image six or seven thousand pounds of wild, tough rhino being transferred at dock side into water-proofed crates which didn't exist?

"I told him that there was no way this could be done; that we had met all the specifications our government required; and that we were going to leave — now! Instantly, we were surrounded by police.

"I asked if I might use the pay phone at dock side and I tried to phone Dr. McClenaghan, Chief of the Contagious Diseases, Health of Animals Division, Department of Agriculture, Ottawa. He had a silent number! I told the operator it was a matter of life or death and that he simply had to be reached since two lives depended on him. I did manage to raise him on that long weekend of the 24th of May, told him our plight and he asked to speak to the veterinarian. It was a most disgruntled doctor who came into the booth. His look implied, 'I'll fix you before you are out of here!'

"Over the phone he had said he was worried because he didn't want the responsibility of the rhinos running loose across the plains of Western Canada, assuming that they were going to break out of their crates!

"After the telephone conversation I told him that he need not worry. We had come too far to have that happen and we pulled away from the dock side. The old truck was pounding on all eight as we made that desperate run for the interior border. Every time we saw a white Quebec Provincial Police car anywhere near us, we were prepared to take the most drastic measures possible not to let the rhinos 'out of the bag'. We did make it into Ontario without being stopped and from there on the road was clear.

"En route we would occasionally play a high jink when we would stop at a garage. The rhinos had to be watered frequently and with warm water. I would ask, as I did at a service station just out of Ottawa, if I might have some warm water. When the attendant asked, 'How much?' I told him I needed about forty gallons. He looked at me and said, 'The radiator of that truck won't take any more than a gallon!' I told him we had two special radiators in the back; that this was a different type of truck; in fact it was nuclear powered. He raced to the back and I swung the door open revealing the huge rhinos behind the vertical bars of the crate.

"The man hastily said, 'Do me a favour, will you? Wait until I phone my wife and get her to come here with her camera. She never believes anything I say, but this time, by golly, I'm going to win!'

"We had to stop every so often along the way, and as we did we found that the rhinos were extremely fond of our common Canadian dandelion. We would gather huge sackfuls along the wayside ditches. Frequently highway patrols would stop to ask us what we were doing, and we would show them our charges. Even to this day the rhinos are as fond of dandelions as they ever were. I dare say that it is their favourite food.''

On our tour through the Alberta Game Farm, we stopped for quite a while before the Markhor goats and the Woodland caribou.

The Markhors are wild goats from the Cabul district of Afghanistan. Magnificent broad spiralled horns distinguish the male of the species. Since these goats are not working for a living, the keepers at the Farm must catch them three times a year and give them a pedicure. Furthermore, *nets* are used, not tranquilizers.

Recently a young fellow was employed at the Game Farm who had previously spent a lot of time working on his uncle's ranch in Saskatchewan. In spite of the warnings of the other ten men involved in the tri-annual round-up, he insisted *he* could straddle the big male and hold him while his hooves were trimmed. The young rancher got on the Markhor's back all right, but within seconds he was catapulted fifteen feet into the air!

The elegant Woodland caribou were the most difficult to capture of all the animals. In actual fact, it took Al Oeming ten years of futility before a bull and two cows were finally caught with nets in very deep early-April snow. The herd currently numbers twenty-four and they continue to enjoy grass, good hay and alfalfa. Al has dubbed the Woodland caribou the ''Harlem Globetrotters of the caribou family''.

Although he didn't say so and I didn't ask, I have a feeling that if Al has any favourites among his animals, they are the Swan Hills grizzlies: Big Dan, Lady Edith and Swanee. When we visited them, they were enjoying their all-time gourmet delight: four-month-old eggs! They receive this special treat only in the fall in preparation for the cold winter ahead.

Dr. Oeming will always be grateful for the capture of this

family of grizzlies to Dan Willier, a veteran Indian trapper from the Drift Pile Reserve.

"Dan had really covered the hills since he was a boy. During the 1950s rabies scare in Alberta, he had the unpleasant task of dumping strychnine poison throughout the hills to rid them of predators.

"Dan knew a lot about grizzlies and I sometimes travelled with him. This friendship was to pay great dividends when, in the spring of 1963, he discovered three orphan cubs in the Virginia Hill section of the Swan Hills. Dan called me and took me to them. I have given the Indians my solemn word that this family of grizzlies will never be separated. We don't have to worry about in-breeding in wild animals within a sixty-year period, so Big Dan mates with his sisters and this is the first cub — Danice. Big Dan is fifteen years old now and weighs over 1,150 pounds — but he still enjoys his daily bottle!"

Al Oeming has gone on many expeditions to gather scientific data on grizzlies. I particularly enjoyed this anecdote.

"I recall an incident just on the western fringe of the Swan Hills. An oil company was drilling at the site and no one was aware that two very large grizzlies were coming nightly to their dump. I went in there just on spec with my Indian helpers. By this time we were generally known and rather cheerfully received. People had heard about our work with the bears, but I have a hunch they felt we were lunatics for wanting to mess around with bears. However, life in an oil drilling camp entails a lot of hard dirty work and these men were always ready for any diversion — particularly if they could get involved.

"I always received great co-operation from camp chiefs and oil company officials and this time I set the trap for a very large bear right down at the company dump. Now, a culvert trap, such as we were using, works on the principle that the bear will poke his head in and, either with a paw or his teeth, pull a bait rod. But he must have sufficient of his body in so that the door drops down behind his massive rear end. I set the trap and began the first night of vigil.

"In the spring you can always set your watch by the time of the first arrival of the bears. Huge — massive — deadly quiet — they come unannounced. At about 8:30 p.m. I nudged Joseph, 'Joe, we had a long trip in and we've been nodding away, what do you see?'

"Joe was trying to focus, blurry-eyed and said, 'It's a horse.'

" 'Look again, Joe.'

"A massive grizzly bear was hovering near a clearing. It is an enormous thrill when you see this huge animal. It was a cool spring night. His warm breath was blowing frosty rings in the evening air. The first thing the bear did was circle the dump. Then he began to pick up the small bait trail leading to the trap — pancakes soaked in blueberry syrup.

"Then that terrifically exciting moment when the grizzly stuck his head inside — that. enormous head the size of a washtub. He brought it out again quickly — went around — tried to rock the trap. He wanted in!

"I knew we could get him but we probably wouldn't until dark, so we kept vigil all night. The bear came back but for some reason or other, he didn't go into the trap.

"So — we set up again for the following evening since the bears stay quietly back in the woods during the day. About midnight the door dropped! It was too dark to see what was going on, but I knew we had the big fellow.

"I told the oil company boys on the night shift that we had the bear and would bring him out, cold-conked with ether, ear-tag him, weigh and measure him. Now the system here was to get at least a pound and a half of commercial ether sprayed in, then get at least twelve strong men — two on each of the six handles welded to the sides of the steel trap — to lug the big monster to a clearing at the edge of the dump. Then, to prolong his sleep, an ordinary funnel that is used to pour gasoline into a tractor, was covered with ether-soaked cotton and placed over his nose. Here we had to be careful or we could drown the bear with ether and cause a respiratory collapse.

"But it still took some persuasion to convince the men at the camp that the bear was now safe to touch. We then had to put great strong nylon ropes on all four paws, make a sling affair and get this onto the big hook of the scale which was attached with huge chains to big clamps and bolted onto a tree. Then came the frantic business of digging under the back of the bear to enable us to get a true weight.

"Well, this was all accomplished and by this time we had at least forty oil workers gathered around the bear. I had all the data I needed. This was a tough old bear with one ear badly ripped. Old bears fight a lot and are all chewed up. His weight was 830 pounds, which is a respectable weight for a spring bear.

"I had placed the tag on his ear when I noticed the grizzly coming to rather rapidly! I told the oil workers that we'd better get out of there — quickly! Behind us, about a hundred feet away, was a very small tool shed. It was right in the middle of the trail that led to the camp proper, but no amount of urging or warning would get those men to move.

" 'Oh,' they said, 'he's got a thousand acres of bush in front of him and that's where he'll go.'

"The bear began to sit on the side of his rump and he started to make some rather ominous noises. I was closest to him and said, 'I think we ought to get out of here. The bear is blinking a lot; he is not foaming at the mouth and he's ready to go . . .'

"No sooner said than done. The big monster wheeled around and with a horrendous bellow, like a deranged bull, charged straight at the mob of men!

"If you can just visualize thirty or forty men all trying to get into a shack that was hard pressed to hold four! And the bear had only about five feet to go to hit that shack. My pants were rolled up because of the mud and I could feel the saliva from his jowls flicking the back of my legs.

"Suddenly — inexplicably — he veered off, hit the bush

and was knocking down poplars that were three inches across. Like a giant brown-furred bulldozer, he careened through the bush.

"The only relaxed man in the whole crowd was a pilot who stood on top of that shack and, with an 8mm camera, filmed the whole proceedings. I still have a copy of that film, and once in a while I look at it and enjoy a good laugh."

My five-hour tour had come to an end, but I know I shall continue to visit the Alberta Game Farm and continue to enjoy the living monument to an outstanding humanist and conservationist, an entertaining story-teller and idol of thousands of students: Dr. Al Oeming.

Progress?
Rhonda Richter

Let's tear down the trees,
Pull up all the flowers,
Flatten the mountains and hills,
Plug up the rivers,
and take out all the fish.
Sell them,
Sell it all,
Make money.

Then let's build condominiums,
grey cement,
blocks of stone,
rows on rows,
forever and ever,
look at the man-made wonder,
Isn't it gorgeous scenery?

Contrast

R. E. Rashley

The sun has set these many hours ago,
And now the moon moves slowly to the west
The city lies below in silent rest,
Her street lamps lending beauty to the snow.
Now all the night is still, and yet we know
That nothing stops — the world goes spinning on,
The same stars shine that lit the Parthenon,
The winds that blew on Babylon still blow.

Man with his vision of divinity
Toils on beneath the shadow of the sword,
His soul in eager strength, his flesh too slow
For deeds immortal. Yet at length, when he
Is but the murmur of an ancient word
The winds that blew on Babylon still blow.

Ecology

M. J. R. Smith

Ecology —
a fancy word
we freely spout
to show
we know
what we're about.
Perhaps a chance
for life
there'll be
if we replace

ecology
with firm
sincere
apology.
Then buckle down
to honest toil
and purify
the choking soil;
clean water, too,
and clear the air,
until the word
ecology
will simply be
mythology.

Sweet Grass
First Western Conservationist
J. W. Grant MacEwan

As the first to propose measures to save the buffalo herds from extinction, Chief Sweet Grass of the Plains Crees might very well be recognized as the pioneer wildlife conservationist of the West. When the Council of the North West Territories met at Livingstone a few months later an ordinance "for the protection of the buffalo" was passed but it was too late, and during the second session of the Council, meeting at Battleford in 1878, the buffalo ordinance was repealed. The once mighty herds moved closer and closer to the brink of total destruction.

In their traditional environment the prairie Indians found buffalo herds in sufficient abundance to meet all needs and saw very little reason to economize. Sometimes they were wasteful and slaughtered beyond all needs. Generally they exercised restraint in killing. The Crees may have been conservation conscious to a greater degree than other prairie tribesmen.

Buffalo tongues were regarded as delicacies and were the ever-present temptation to slaughter ruthlessly for the sake of these choice morsels but Cree women — showing the good sense typical of their sex — protested when the number of tongues brought in by the hunters represented more carcass meat than could be saved or utilized. The same Crees never killed young beavers found in a lodge. White trappers, greedy for furs, might take all the beaver inhabitants but the Cree hunters aimed to turn back the young ones to mature and propagate.

It was not surprising, therefore, that it was a Cree who advised the incoming white men to go easy on the buffalo. It was during the Fort Pitt discussions preceding the second stage signing of Treaty Number Six, in September 1876, that Sweet Grass made his plea to save the herds. Already buffalo numbers had been reduced to a fraction and the reasons were clear to the Chief. With a profitable market for buffalo hides and superior rifles available for the killing, both Indian and white hunters were out to take advantage. The wild animals, which had numbered millions so recently, could not withstand the new pressures and Chief Sweet Grass was issuing a solemn warning. It may be presumed that he had never heard of game laws in other parts of the world but his proposal for the safeguard of remaining members of the buffalo race was no less clear. If white hide-hunters were inclined to slaughter without conscience and were influencing Indians to do the same, it was up to the white rulers to take steps to halt the destruction. If the white man could make and enforce laws, this was a proper time and reason. Facing Lieutenant-Governor Morris, the Chief asked for an Act or Ordinance which would have the effect of ending or curtailing the slaughter. He may have realized that it was already too late because he added his intention of settling on a piece of land and trying to farm.

But the real reason for the Chief's presence at Fort Pitt on that occasion was to discuss the proposed treaty. He and his people had been absent on a hunt when the proceedings were scheduled to begin but the Commissioners, acting upon wise advice, agreed to defer until their return. In due course, Sweet Grass and his Crees arrived at Fort Pitt and the meeting got under way.

Pakan from White Fish Lake and Sweet Grass were the obvious Indian leaders and it was Sweet Grass — lover of peace and unashamed to admit it — who set the tone for the Fort Pitt conference. Facing the Lieutenant-Governor from Manitoba, he thanked the Queen for sending the Commissioners to discuss terms for a treaty. Standing erect and fearless, he won the admiration of Indians and whites alike. He talked like a man who wanted no trouble but would fight for justice. "May the white man's blood never be spilt on this soil," he said. "I am thankful that the white man and red man can stand together. . . . Let us be as one. Do your utmost to help me and help my children so that they may prosper."

He acknowledged confidence that the proposed treaty would provide fairly for his people and open the door to a new world for them. Nevertheless, he wanted time to consider the terms suggested by Lieutenant-Governor Morris.

After a few days, Sweet Grass was ready to report his conclusions. Indians gathered in a big semi-circle, facing the Commissioners. It was an auspicious setting. Autumn colours brought beauty to the entire river valley. The mid-September sun was hot enough to induce young braves to appear in loin-cloths but not hot enough to make visiting Commissioners want to remove any part of their top-hat attire.

With dignity in his bearing, Chief Sweet Grass strode to the place reserved for speakers. All eyes were upon him, including those of the sultry Chief Big Bear who had remained annoyingly silent throughout the conference days. Big Bear was powerful and defiant and it was quite obvious that he would not be signing the Treaty — not for some time, anyway. His presence might have been expected to make it difficult for Sweet Grass to speak freely but Sweet Grass was a man who answered only to his own conscience.

Making sure that Big Bear heard his words, Sweet Grass said he believed the coming of the Queen's representatives had been ordered by the Great Spirit. Major change in the Indian way of life was now inescapable. It was up to the native people to make the best of the new circumstances. Turning his face toward Big Bear, he said: "Think of our children and all who will follow us. There is hope for them here. Say 'yes' and take the Governor's hand."

With the Sweet Grass help and influence, Treaty Number Six was brought to a successful conclusion and treaty money was paid. And it was in March of the following year that the new Council of the North West Territories, meeting with Lieutenant-Governor David Laird, passed the Ordinance for protection of the Buffalo. It was in the spirit of the Sweet Grass plea but not much could be done at that point to stem the awful decline. Three years later, the wild herd had, for all practical purposes, disappeared. The sighting of a single buffalo was a rare experience. Only a few head in captivity and some millions of tons of whitened bones strewn across the prairies remained to remind Indians and others of the damage men with guns are capable of doing.

Perhaps the destruction of the great wild herds was necessary in any plan for land settlement but, nevertheless, the Sweet Grass plea for restraint marked the Chief as a man of vision and wisdom.

The Sun
Dana Gorbahn

The sun is hot;
It lightens the earth brightly
    And no one owns it.

The Cattle Thief

E. Pauline Johnson

They were coming across the prairie, they were galloping
    hard and fast;
For the eyes of those desperate riders had sighted their
    man at last —
Sighted him off to Eastward, where the Cree encampment
    lay,
Where the cottonwoods fringed the river, miles and miles
    away.
Mistake him? Never! Mistake him? the famous Eagle
    Chief!
That terror to all the settlers, that desperate Cattle
    Thief —
That monstrous, fearless Indian, who lorded it over
    the plain,
Who thieved and raided, and scouted, who rode like a
    hurricane!
But they've tracked him across the prairie; they've
    followed him hard and fast;
For those desperate English settlers have sighted their
    man at last.

Up they wheeled to the tepees, all their British blood
    aflame,
Bent on bullets and bloodshed, bent on bringing down their
    game;
But they searched in vain for the Cattle Thief: that
    lion had left his lair,
And they cursed like a troop of demons — for the women alone
    were there.
"The sneaking Indian coward," they hissed; "he hides while
    yet he can;

He'll come in the night for cattle, but he's scared to
    face a *man*."
"Never!" and up from the cottonwoods rang the voice of
    Eagle Chief;
And right out into the open stepped, unarmed, the Cattle
    Thief.
Was that the game they had coveted? Scarce fifty years
    had rolled
Over that fleshless, hungry frame, starved to the bone and
    old;
Over that wrinkled, tawny skin, unfed by the warmth of
    blood.
Over those hungry, hollow eyes that glared for the sight
    of food.

He turned, like a hunted lion: "I know not fear," said
    he;
And the words outleapt from his shrunken lips in the
    language of the Cree.
"I'll fight you, white-skins, one by one, till I kill you
    all," he said;
But the threat was scarcely uttered, ere a dozen balls of
    lead
Whizzed through the air about him like a shower of metal
    rain,
And the gaunt old Indian Cattle Thief dropped dead on the
    open plain.
And that band of cursing settlers gave one triumphant
    yell,
And rushed like a pack of demons on the body that writhed
    and fell.
"Cut the fiend up into inches, throw his carcass on the
    plain;
Let the wolves eat the cursed Indian, he'd have treated us
    the same."

A dozen hands responded, a dozen knives gleamed high,
But the first stroke was arrested by a woman's strange,
    wild cry.
And out into the open, with a courage past belief,
She dashed, and spread her blanket o'er the corpse of
    the Cattle Thief;
And the words outleapt from her shrunken lips in the
    language of the Cree,
"If you mean to touch that body, you must cut your way
    through *me*."
And that band of cursing settlers dropped backward one
    by one,
For they knew that an Indian woman roused, was a woman
    to let alone.
And then she raved in a frenzy that they scarcely
    understood,
Raved of the wrongs she had suffered since her earliest
    babyhood:
"Stand back, stand back, you white-skins, touch that dead
    man to your shame;
You have stolen my father's spirit, but his body I only
    claim.
You have killed him, but you shall not dare to touch him
    now he's dead.
You have cursed, and called him a Cattle Thief, though
    you robbed him first of bread —
Robbed him and robbed my people — look there, at that
    shrunken face,
Starved with a hollow hunger, we owe to you and your race.
What have you left to us of land, what have you left of
    game,
What have you brought but evil, and curses since you
    came?
How have you paid us for our game? how paid us for
    our land?

By a *book,* to save our souls from the sins *you* brought
    in your other hand.
Go back with your new religion, we never have
    understood
Your robbing an Indian's *body,* and mocking his *soul*
    with food.
Go back with your new religion, and find — if find you
    can —
The *honest* man you have ever made from out a *starving*
    man.
You say your cattle are not ours, your meat is not our
    meat;
When *you* pay for the land you live in, *we'll* pay for the
    meat we eat.
Give back our land and our country, give back our herds
    of game;
Give back the furs and the forests that were ours before
    you came;
Give back the peace and the plenty. Then come with your
    new belief,
And blame, if you dare, the hunger that *drove* him to be
    a thief."

The Ruffs and the Hootles

Mervyn J. Huston

Once upon a time there lived side by side two tribes, the Ruffs
and the Hootles. They got along very well for many years until
someone noticed that the Ruffs had blue eyes and the Hootles
had green eyes. Then it was realized that the Ruffs combed their
hair forward and the Hootles backwards. There wasn't much
that could be done by either group about the defective eye color
of the other but each made strenuous efforts to correct the stupid

way the other combed his hair. This led to bitterness and finally both sides took up their spears to protect their own way of life and bring enlightenment to the others.

There was a great war and many people were killed. However, neither side prevailed and finally the two tribes retired to opposite sides of a river with the Ruffs in the east and the Hootles in the west. Although the fighting ceased, each tribe from time to time would line up on the bank of the river and shout diploms (insults) at those on the opposite bank. This became known as diplomacy. Since the river was wide and it was difficult to hear the diploms, the tribes agreed to meet for this purpose on a small island called Un. This worked very well and the quality of the diploms increased considerably. Other tribes became interested and sent delegates to listen to the fun and to add a few diploms of their own.

This satisfactory state of affairs was not to continue because of two important scientific discoveries. One was the discovery of the wheel and the other of the bow and arrow. Neither tribe was able to gain a marked advantage over the other in these fields because each knew quite a bit about what was happening on the other side of the river. They got the information by buying it from venal members of the other tribe. Also, every once in a while a member of a tribe would decide he was combing his hair the wrong way and would cross over to the other side taking with him all the information he could collect. In many respects the level of culture of these tribes was quite advanced.

Both groups recognized the horrible destructive power of the bow and arrow and agreed that if this terrible weapon were ever unleashed it would mean the complete and utter destruction of their entire world. They discussed this on the island of Un and each side recommended that the other side throw away their bows and arrows. Nothing came of this. They did, however, sign an agreement that these weapons would be used only on wart-hogs and ubalos and not on each other.

This agreement did not prevent them from tinkering with the weapon and making bigger and bigger bows (for defensive purposes). When one tribe, say the Hootles, had made a new big bow they would beat on a gong and the Ruffs would come down to the river bank to watch them shoot it. The Hootles would be very careful not to shoot their arrows where they would fall on the Ruffs. For one thing they didn't want the Ruffs to know what kind of arrows they were using and for another they didn't want to start a row just yet. The arrow would be shot straight up in the air and all the Hootles would cheer and shout derisive diploms across the river. This was said to be demonstrating brack (goodwill). The Ruffs would hurry back to their workshops and make a bigger and better bow and the process would be repeated.

Occasionally something would go wrong and the arrow would just fall on the ground. When this happened there was great consternation and humiliation. The tribe would call a meeting of the clabber (governing body) and there would be a great deal of fiery oratory and buck-passing. Someone would then be selected as a sacrifice (usually the person who knew the most about arrow making) and when the gods had thereby been propitiated, things would carry on exactly as before.

The bows got bigger and bigger until one day the Hootles attached a mouse to the arrow and shot it right out of sight. The Ruffs countered by attaching a wart-hog to their next arrow. The Hootles replied with a ubalo. Finally the Ruffs shot a man attached to an arrow right into the middle of the surrounding jungle and he was never heard from again. This was a great victory for the Ruffs until the Hootles fired off a man and a woman. The idea was that they would be company for each other when they arrived. Nothing came of this because they landed on their heads in a swamp and were eaten by crocodiles. But it was a great triumph nevertheless.

Both sides of the river were lined with huge bows and arrows trained on the other shore. The leaders of each tribe swore solemnly they had no intention of using them and would take them down just as soon as the other side did.

While all this was going on, both tribes were experimenting with the wheel and applying it to various kinds of vehicles. The Hootles enjoyed this sort of activity particularly and became very skillful at making fancy chariots with gold fronts and ornate tops. Every Hootle tribesman insisted on having a fancy chariot to run around in and to impress his neighbours. These were very expensive, so the workers formed grabs (unions) which went to the chiefs to demand more and more wump (money) so each man could have a chariot. The chiefs protested loudly and refused. The tribesmen stopped working until the chiefs agreed. The men were surprised how easily this worked and the grabs returned to the chiefs many times. The cost of the chariots went up and up and so did the cost of bows and arrows. It became necessary to reduce the work on the bows and arrows to satisfy the demand for chariots. The Hootle chiefs had to rely more and more on diplomacy in their dealings with the Ruffs.

The Ruffs on the other hand did not permit any grabs. Anybody who suggested one was hung by the heels in the market place. The Ruffs made a few chariots, but only for transporting bows and arrows about. They devoted most of their energy to making weapons.

One morning a Hootle named Bloob was on sentry duty at the river's edge. He had been up all night drinking foom with a hot-chariot group and was feeling pretty skuble (rocky). He gazed across the river and saw what he thought was an arrow fly from the land of the Ruffs. It was really a zibble-bird but he was not focussing very clearly. He shouted wildly and let fly his arrow. The other Hootles jumped to their bows and followed suit. None of the arrows reached the other side but the Ruffs saw them coming and fired in return. The Ruffs' arrows were very powerful and numerous and killed most of the Hootles including Bloob. The Ruffs then came across the river on rafts and carried back the Hootles' gold chariots and women.

However, up the river a short distance was a tribe called the

Bugwoodus who had brown eyes and combed their hair sideways. They were therefore considered very ignorant and primitive by the Ruffs and Hootles. When the Bugwoodus saw that the Hootles had been destroyed and that the Ruffs had fired off all their arrows they came down with their old fashioned spears and killed all the Ruffs.

Thus peace returned again to the jungle and the Bugwoodus lived happily ever after.

The First Fire-Flowers

John S. Morgan

In Indian legend, fire-flowers, which grow in such abundance that they sometimes blanket entire hillsides with their red blossoms, sprang from the blood of courageous young warriors. This is the story.

Thousands of years ago, fierce conflicts between the southern tribes and those of the north raged up and down the coastal regions of British Columbia, their dispute centering over the possession of an island, now called the Island of Dead Men. Its name is appropriate, for, at one time, the waters encircling it ran red with the blood of the slain.

At last, the southern tribes lured the northern warriors far out to sea. Then, in their absence, a war party of the south returned under cover of night; raided the enemy camps; seized the women, the children and the old men too feeble for battle; and carried them to the Island of Dead Men.

When they realized that they had been duped by their enemy, the warriors of the north, in rage and frustration, launched wave after wave of war canoes upon the island in a valiant attempt to rescue their loved ones. The air was filled with arrows, the shrieks and lamentations of the imprisoned, and the groans of the dying. At first, the waves of northern warriors seemed to strike in vain; again and again, they were repulsed, only to gather force once more in a desperate onslaught on the foe. But after persistent attacks, one of the bravest and most respected of the southern warriors lifted up his hand and shouted across the waters:

"O men of the north, long have we stood up against you, but your numbers are greater than ours. Each day, there are fewer of us. Each day, our food supplies grow less, for in addition to ourselves, we are feeding our prisoners — your fathers and mothers, wives, and children. Hear, then, the terms which we, though weakened by battle, are still able to enforce. We will fight on, whatever your decision. Tomorrow we will kill all our prisoners. The only way that you can save them is by giving for each prisoner one of your bravest, strongest warriors. These will be put to death in their stead. Are you willing to accept these terms in order to save those you love?"

From the ring of northern canoes encircling the embattled warriors of the south arose a confusion of voices.

"I do not care what happens to me, but spare my young son."

"Let my daughter go free. I will willingly die in her place."

"Take me, but spare my father."

From the many who offered themselves, 200, the bravest and the best, were chosen.

In deference to the courage displayed by these valiant warriors, the circle of canoes fortifying the island gave way to allow them passageway to the shore. Here they stepped forth, shoulders erect, heads high, eyes flashing defiance at the enemy.

Honouring their part of the compact, the southern warriors quickly herded the old men, women, and children into the canoes. Some tried in vain to break from the strong arms of their captors, preferring to join their husbands or sons in death rather than live without them.

Forming a long line before the southern warriors, these valiant young men bent down, only for a moment, to lay their bows and arrows at their feet. Then they stood, erect and unflinching to await death.

The next morning when the people of the south returned to the scene of havoc which they had wrought, they found that hundreds of brilliant flowers the colour of blood had sprung up overnight. The Sagalie Tyee had placed them there in honour of the fallen warriors.

This is the origin of the fire-flower, an everlasting remembrance of these valiant northern warriors, which now adorns the hills and wooded areas of our land.

The Intruders
Phyllis Gertrude Rodd

Between the shores of the small deep bay, clear green water mirrored the tall firs and arbutus. A woman sat on the beach tending a campfire beside a tent, while two children in brief bathing suits clambered over the rocky shore, calling excitedly to each other at every new discovery. Behind them, in a small clearing, a man was building a house, and the rafters showed bright against the dark trees. A big black dog ran back and forth, to the woman, to the man, and around the children.

"What are they doing?"

A small brown face peered out under the root of the arbutus. The pointed nose, two bright black eyes, and trembling whiskers of a mink turned in dismay toward his brother. The other young mink looked across the still waters of the narrow bay.

"They are building a nest," he answered wisely.

"Are they going to live there?" The more timid one crept back into the shadows.

"Yes, I think so. More and more of them are coming. They are building their nests all along the water's edge."

"What are they called?" asked the little mink.

"Their name is Man."

That night, the animals who lived around the bay held a meeting by the biggest fir tree. All had been summoned. The gulls cried the news, and the kingfisher kept repeating it during the day. Finally, when the light had gone out in the tent on the beach, all the creatures came to the fir, by secret paths.

The sea birds — gulls and kingfishers — sat high up on the branches. The small birds — juncos, sparrows, nuthatches — jumped about from branch to branch, then settled down in a row beneath the sea birds. A pair of hummingbirds, almost invisible, sat on the end of a twig. The owl, quiet, with unblinking eyes, perched just above the kingfishers, while near the top of the tree sat a heron, thin and hunched against the golden moon. These were the birds who lived in the trees around the bay.

On a lower branch were three squirrels, chattering.

"My cousin lives beside Man," one said, "and is very well fed, with nuts of many kinds and bread and porridge." The small birds listened carefully.

"My cousin," said another squirrel, "was caught by a cat." The small birds chirped and fluttered.

"This Man doesn't have a cat," said the third squirrel. "Just a large black dog. Anyone can see it coming."

"They will have a cat, you'll see," said the second squirrel. "They always do, to keep down the mice."

There was a sudden scurry and then silence among the leaves at the roots of the tree, and a tiny gray mouse squeaked, "Someone must protect us!"

By this time, more animals were arriving at the meeting place. A family of raccoons, mother, father, and four small ones, sat in a row on a log. The two small mink, one dark brown, the other golden, came with their parents and an old grandfather who had once been the pride of the bay with his light coat, now so faded and shabby. They sat down beside the coons, who moved farther away.

"Are we all here?" asked the owl.

"Yes," said a soft voice, as the deer and doe moved quietly into the circle. "We are all here except the King."

"We must not be afraid," cautioned the owl, as the coons twittered to each other. "We are to obey the rules of the meeting."

"Here he comes," whispered a mink.

Through the dark shadows, a pale sinewy form appeared, moving like liquid over the fallen logs and leaves. The green eyes in the broad head looked at the small quiet creatures.

"Peace," said the cougar, and took his place before them.

There was silence for a moment, then the owl hooted and said, slowly, "We have met here to decide what should be done about this Man who has come to our bay."

The bright eyes of the cougar moved around the circle of animals and up to the branches of the tree, then closed languidly.

"I know what I could do," he said, and ran a red tongue around his lips. "One by one. They are so weak."

"If you did that," said a new deep voice, and all the animals jumped in fright, "if you did that, then more Men would come and hunt you to the finish."

The cougar turned and looked into the shadows. "Come forward," he said. "Let us see who you are."

The black dog moved into the circle.

"This is my home too," he said. "I have a right to come to this meeting."

"Peace," said the cougar, while all the animals and birds looked at the dog.

"It is right," said the owl, "that Man should be here to decide his future."

"I am not of Man," said the dog. "I just live with him."

"Why?" asked the cougar.

The dog paused. "I always have," he said. "He feeds me and brushes me, and I bark at strangers."

(The small mink whispered to his brother. "I wouldn't like Man to touch *me*. All those hairless, white fingers!")

"Then you will be considered Man," said the cougar.

The dog bowed his head in agreement and said nothing.

"Let us hear the plea," continued the cougar.

The owl hooted, and all were quiet.

"We, the creatures of this territory, have gathered to decide the future of the Intruders who nest unbidden on the shores of our bay. Whatever we do must be done by all. Whatever we suffer must be suffered by all. We must unite until they have been driven away, or we must leave them in peace. What is our decision? Will each member speak?"

The heron moved his great wings. "They will not bother me," he said. "I can go away when they awake and return when they sleep. I have other haunts. Let them stay unharmed."

"One to stay," said the owl.

The gulls looked at each other. "They have bread and scraps," they said, "and the young ones have not yet thrown rocks at us. We are content. Let them stay unharmed."

"Two to stay," said the owl.

The kingfisher ruffled his feathers. "The nest they are building has a high steady top from which I can see into the depths of the water where the fish hide. It is good. Let them stay unharmed."

"Three to stay," said the owl.

A junco fluttered his tail and chirped. "I speak for the small birds," he said. "We do not want them. They will look for our nests, cut down the trees, burn up the leaves where our food is, and eat the berries. I know, for I have lived near them before. They must go."

"No," said a chickadee. "In the winter they give us crumbs and suet in the snow. We fly to their nests to shelter from the cold, and they do no harm to us."

"You small birds," said the owl, sternly, "have you not decided yet amongst yourselves? Who is now to speak?"

The hummingbird flew down before the face of the cougar, who drew back. Hovering, wings whirring, the tiny bird said,

"Once, I was held and fed by Man. Water and honey was given to me when I was stunned and dying. He saved my life. Let him stay."

"We will agree," said the junco. "The small birds agree. Let him stay unharmed."

"Four to stay," said the owl.

"We do not really mind," said the squirrel. "If they do give nuts and porridge and bread, that will be very good, a change from acorns; and we can keep out of their way."

"Five to stay."

The cougar's tail twitched but he said nothing.

The deer pawed the ground. "We have been hunted," he said. "We have been hounded." The dog hung his head. "Run from cover to cover with guns, and kept from our food by cruel wires. Our country is not our own now, and we must move farther and farther away every year. We do not wish harm to Man. We wish only peace and a place of our own away from him. Let him go away."

"Five to stay, one to go," said the owl.

The cougar raised his head.

The raccoons chirruped among themselves as they sat on the log, paws folded, looking slyly at one another. The father spoke.

"We have lived very well without Man, and could live very well with Man, as some of my brothers have done successfully. But sometimes Man is selfish and keeps his fruits for himself; then we suffer and are shot. Let him go."

"Five to stay, two to go." The owl stepped from foot to foot, and the cougar rippled his great shoulders.

The old mink moved slowly forward. "I have lived here for a long time," he said, "and shall not see many more springs. Like all old things, I do not want change, and my ways are wild always. All my family are of the shadows. This has been our home, as safe as any. Men may set traps for us — our fur is valuable. They have no fur of their own."

"(Only on their heads,)" said the young mink.

"We can do very little to drive them away," continued the old mink, "except to shriek on the beach at night to frighten the young. I speak for the mink. Let them go."

"Three to go, five to stay," said the owl. "Now you small ones, mice, shrews, and rats."

"I speak for us," said a muskrat. "For me, too, they will set traps. All our family can help to drive them away. The mice can chew through anything and cause destruction. The rats can bring a plague, if so you wish, and a shrew or two in the well can be very distressing for them." There was a sharp squeak. "Only if you are needed," continued the muskrat. "We muskrats and common rats could chew the wood under the nests. Let them go." And all the small mice squealed in agreement.

"Five to stay, four to go. Of our people, the cougar and myself yet to speak."

"And we insects," buzzed a wasp. "We insects speak."

"What do you say?" asked the owl.

"This is our desire. We despise Man. We shall see that he is stung if he slaps us, we wasps, we bees, we mosquitoes, and these small creeping things. So we say, let him cease."

"Five to stay, five to go."

"I will speak last," said the cougar, "for I am the King."

"Let there be no fear," said the owl, stretching his wings. "I am not troubled by Man, nor do I need him. I say, let him go."

"Five to stay, six to go," snarled the cougar. "Now let us hear from Man."

The dog shook himself. He looked around at all the animals, quietly waiting for his word.

"My people have come here to make their home. They are good and kind. They have no guns or traps; they love the woods and all its creatures. They will feed you and shelter you from the cold, if there is any need, and they do no harm to anything.

"I have lived on city streets where there are no leaves, no grass, no trees, and all is hard as rock on my paws. I, also, will be happier here and hurt no one unless I am forced." He looked at the coons, who moved away. "So do I decide for Man. We shall stay."

The cougar swished his tail. "Six to go and six to stay. I have the deciding vote.

"You know what I must say. Man has come, and we must accept him and all he brings. This is my Kingdom, and I do not want to leave even a small part, but if Man stays, then I must go. If I am seen, once, beside their nest, then men with guns and dogs will come and bring terror for everyone, for all my small creatures. It has happened before in other parts of my Kingdom. We cannot war with Man. We can only hope that Man will not war with us. I say farewell to you. Man will stay, but I must go." The cougar bent his head.

After a moment, the owl hooted. "This, then, is our decision. Seven to stay, six to go. Man will stay, unharmed, and we must agree to accept his presence. Those who cannot live with him, must move away; those who can, must be good neighbors."

The dog spoke. "They will be kind to you, as I will."

"We are agreed?" asked the owl.

All the animals cried, "Agreed!"

The cougar walked quietly away, but just before he disappeared among the dark trees, he turned, and looking around, spoke softly to the silent animals.

"I say farewell to you, and will not come back. Let there be peace in this part of my Kingdom."

After he had gone, one by one, the animals left the meeting place.

Later, in the tent on the beach, the man turned and woke. Putting his hand out of the sleeping bag, he felt the soft black head.

"Good boy, good dog," he murmured.

WildLife?

The Bear at Camp

Beatrice C. Rowley

Fumbling and sniffling at the discard pile
He came by cover of the autumn dark
To see what he might rummage to his taste
And by such insolence became the mark
Of outraged hoots and cries, and one well-flung
Indignant boot. We did not see his eyes,
But from his blundering and swift retreat
Imagined they were widened with surprise.

These woods are his. Have been for how long now?
Too long to count at least, if bears could count.
And what are we queer creatures doing here,
Loafing among his ferns, beside his fount
Of crimson berries, with our alien smell
Polluting earth's sweet, mouldy, wild perfume?
It needs some higher court here to decide
Exactly who is trespassing on whom.

This Is My Bear

James Oliver Curwood

It was the week of the Big Festival when David and his Métis arrived at Towaskook's village. Towaskook was the "farthest east" of the totem-worshippers, and each of his forty or fifty people reminded David of the devil-chaser on the canvas of the Snow Fox's tepee. They were dressed up, as he remarked to the Métis, "like friends". Towaskook himself was disguised in a huge bear head from which protruded a pair of buffalo horns that had somehow drifted up here from the western prairies, and it was his special incumbency to perform various antics about his totem-pole for at least six hours between sunrise and sunset, chanting all the time most dolorous supplications to the squat monster who sat grinning at the top of it. The Festival had reached its fourth *kesikow* — or day — when David came. It was "the day of good hunting", and Towaskook and his people worked themselves into exhaustion in the ardour of their prayers that the game of the mountains might walk right up to their tepee doors to be killed, thus necessitating the smallest possible physical exertion in its capture. That night Towaskook visited David at his camp a little up the river to see what he could get out of the white man. He was monstrously fat — fat from laziness; and David wondered how he had managed to put in his hours of labour under the totem-pole. David sat in silence, trying to make out something from their gestures, as his Métis Jacques and the old chief talked.

Jacques repeated it all to him after Towaskook had risen from his squat position, sighing deeply, and had left them. It was a terrible journey over those mountains, Towaskook had said. He had been on the Stickine once. He had split with his tribe, and had started eastward with twice that many followers, but a half of them had died — died because they would not leave their precious totems behind, and so had been caught in a deep snow that came early. It was a ten days' journey over the mountains. You went up above the clouds — many times you had to go above the clouds. He would never make the journey again. There was one chance — just one. He had a young bear-hunter, Kio. His face was still smooth. He had not won his spurs, so to speak, and he was anxious to perform a great feat, especially as he was in love with his medicine-man's daughter Kwak-wa-Pisew, The Butterfly. Kio might go, to prove his valiancy to The Butterfly. Towaskook had gone for him. Of course, on a mission of this kind, Kio would accept no pay. That would go to Towaskook. The two hundred dollars' worth of supplies satisfied him.

A little later Towaskook returned with Kio. Kio was exceedingly youthful, slim built as a weasel, but with a deep-set and treacherous eye. He listened. He would go. He would go as far as the confluence of the Pitman and the Stickine, if Towaskook would assure him The Butterfly. Towaskook, eyeing greedily the supplies which Jacques had laid out alluringly, nodded an agreement to that. "The next day," Kio said then, eager now for adventure. "The next day they would start."

That night Jacques carefully made up the two shoulder-packs which David and Kio were to carry, for thereafter their travel would be entirely afoot. David's burden, with his rifle, was fifty pounds. Jacques saw them off, shouting a last warning for David to "keep a watch on that devil-eyed Kio".

Kio was not like his eyes. He turned out, very shortly, to be a communicable and rather likeable young fellow. He was ignorant of the white man's talk. But he was a master of gesticulation; and when, in climbing their first mountain, David discovered muscles in his legs and back that he had never known of before Kio laughingly sympathized with him and assured him in vivid pantomime that he would soon get used to it. Their first night they camped almost at the summit of the mountain. Kio wanted to make the warmth of the valley beyond, but those new muscles in David's legs and back declared otherwise. Strawberries were ripening in the deeper valleys, but up where they were it was cold. A bitter wind came off the snow on the peaks, and David could smell the pungent fog of the clouds. They were so high that the scrub-twigs of their fire smouldered with scarcely sufficient heat to fry their bacon. David was oblivious of discomfort. His blood ran warm with hope and anticipation. He was almost at the end of his journey. It had been a great fight, and he had won. There was no doubt in his mind now. After this he could face the world again.

Day after day they made their way westward. It was tremendous, this journey over the backbone of the mountains. It gave one a different conception of the vastness of things, and of the pygmy insignificance of men. They were like ants on these mountains, David thought — insignificant, crawling ants. Here was where one might find a soul and a religion if he had never had one before. One's littleness was appalling. At times it was almost frightening. It made one think, impressed upon one that life was not much more than an accident in this vast scale of creation, and that there was great necessity for a God. In Kio's eyes, as he sometimes looked down into the valleys, there was this thing; the thought which perhaps he couldn't analyse, the great truth which he couldn't understand, but felt. It made a worshipper of him — a devout worshipper of the totem. And it occurred to David that the spirit of God must be in that totem even as much as in finger-worn rosaries and the ivory crosses on women's breasts.

Early on the eleventh day they came to the confluence of the Pitman and the Stickine rivers and a little later Kio turned back on his homeward journey, and David and his dog Baree were alone. This aloneness fell upon them like a thing that had a pulse and was alive. They had crossed the Divide, and were in a great sunlit country of amazing beauty and grandeur, with wide valleys between the mountains. It was July. From up and down the valley, from the breaks between the peaks and from the little gullies cleft in shale and rock that crept up to the snow-lines, came a soft and droning murmur. It was the music of running water. That music was always in the air, for the rivers, the creeks and the tiny streams gushing down from the snow that lay eternally up near the clouds, were never still. There were sweet perfumes as well as music in the air. The earth was bursting with green; the early flowers were turning the sunny slopes into coloured splashes of red and white and purple; splashes of violets, of forget-me-nots, and wild asters and hyacinths. David looked upon it all, and his soul drank in its wonders. He made his camp, and he remained in it all that day and the next. He was eager to go on, and yet in his eagerness he hesitated and waited. It seemed to him that he must become acquainted with this empty world before venturing farther into it — alone; that it was necessary for him to understand it a little, and get his bearings. He could not lose himself. Jacques had assured him of that, and Kio had pantomimed it, pointing many times at the broad, shallow stream that was ahead of him. All he had to do was to follow the river. In time, many weeks of course, it would bring him to the white settlement on the ocean. Long before that he would strike Firepan Creek. Kio had never been that far; he had never been farther than this junction of the two streams, Towaskook had informed Jacques. So it was not fear that held David. It was the *aloneness*. He was taking a long mental breath. And meanwhile he was repairing his boots, and doctoring Baree's feet, bruised and sore by their travel over the shale of the mountain tops.

He thought that he had experienced the depths of loneliness after leaving the missioner. But here it was a much larger thing. This first night, as he sat under the stars and a great white moon, with Baree at his feet, it engulfed him; not in a depressing way, but awesomely. It was not an unpleasant loneliness, and yet he felt that it had no depths, no measurement. It was as vast as the mountains that shut him in.

Somewhere, miles to the east of him now, was Kio. That was all. He knew that he would never be able to describe it, this loneliness — or aloneness; one man and a dog, with a world to themselves. After a little, as he looked up at the stars and listened to the droning sound of the waters in the valley, it began to thrill him with a new kind of intelligence. Here was peace as vast as space itself. It was not troubled by the struggling existence of men and women, and it seemed to him that he must remain very still under the watchfulness of those billions of sentinels in the sky, with the white moon floating slowly under them. The second night he made himself and Baree a small fire. The third morning he shouldered his pack and went on.

Baree kept close to his master's side, and the eyes of the two were constantly on the alert. They were in splendid game country, and David watched for the first opportunity that would give Baree and himself fresh meat. The white sandbars and gravelly shores of the stream were covered with the tracks of the wild dwellers of the valley and the adjoining ranges, and Baree sniffed hungrily whenever he came to the warm scent of last night's spoor. He was hungry. He had been hungry all the way over the mountains. Three times that day David saw caribou at a distance. In the afternoon he saw a grizzly on a green slope. Toward evening he ran into luck. A band of sheep had come down from a mountain to drink, and he came upon them suddenly, the wind in his favour. He killed a young ram. For a full minute after firing the shot he stood in his tracks, scarcely breathing. The report of his rifle was like an explosion. It leaped from mountain to mountain, echoing, deepening, coming back to him in murmuring intonations, and dying out at last in a sighing gasp. It was a weird and disturbing sound. He fancied, at first, that it could be heard many miles away. Then he went to the sheep, and that night the two feasted on fresh meat.

It was their fifth day in the valley when they came to a break in the western wall of the range, and through this break flowed a stream that was very much like the Stickine, broad and shallow and ribboned with shifting bars of sand. David made up his mind that it must be the Firepan, and he could feel his pulse quicken as he set up it with Baree. He must be quite near to Tavish's cabin, if it had not been destroyed. Even if it had been burned on account of the plague that had infested it he would surely discover the charred ruins of it. It was three o'clock when he started up the creek, and he was — inwardly — tremendously agitated. He grew more and more positive that he was close to the end of his adventure. He would soon come upon life — human life. And then? He tried to dispel the unsteadiness of his emotions, the swiftly growing discomfort of a great anxiety. The first, of course, would be Tavish's cabin, or the ruins of it. He had taken it for granted that Tavish would be here, near the confluence of the two streams. A hunter or prospector would naturally choose that location. And not far beyond where Tavish had lived. . . .

He travelled slowly, questing both sides of the stream, and listening. He expected at any moment to hear a sound, a new kind of sound. And he also scrutinized closely the clean, white bars of sand. There were footprints in them of the wild things. Once his heart gave a sudden jump when he saw a bear-track that looked very much like a moccasin track. It was a wonderful bear country. Their signs were everywhere along the stream, and their number and freshness made Baree restless. David travelled until dark. He had the desire to go on even then. He built a small fire instead, and cooked his supper. For a long time after that he sat in the moonlight smoking his pipe, and still listening. He tried not to think. The next day would settle his doubts — Tavish, the girl, what he would find. He went to sleep late and awoke with the summer dawn.

The stream grew narrower and the country wilder as he progressed. It was noon when Baree stopped dead in his tracks, stiff-legged, the bristles of his spine erect, a low and ominous growl in his throat. He was standing over a patch of white sand no larger than a blanket.

"What is it, boy?" said David.

He went to him casually, and stood for a moment at the edge of the sand without looking down, lighting his pipe.

"What is it?"

The next moment his heart seemed rising up into his throat. He had been expecting what his eyes looked upon now, and he had been watching for it, but he had not anticipated such a tremendous shock. The imprint of a moccasined foot in the sand! There was no doubt of it this time. A human foot had made it — one, two, three, four, five times in crossing that patch of sand! He stood with the pipe in his mouth; staring down, apparently without power to move or breathe. It was a small footprint. Like a boy's. He noticed then, with slowly shifting eyes, that Baree was bristling and growling over another track. A bear track, huge, deeply impressed in the sand. The beast's great spoor crossed the outer edge of the sand, following the direction of the moccasin tracks. It was thrillingly fresh, if Baree's bristling spine and rumbling voice meant anything.

David's eyes followed the direction of the two trails. A hundred yards up-stream he could see where gravel and rock were replaced entirely by sand, quite a wide, unbroken sweep of it, across which those clawed and moccasined feet must have travelled if they had followed the creek. He was not interested in the bear, and Baree was not interested in the Indian boy, so when they came to the sand one followed the moccasin tracks and the other the claw tracks. They were not at any time more than ten feet apart. And then, all at once, they came together, and David saw that bear had crossed the sand last and that his huge paws had obliterated a part of the moccasin trail. This did not strike him as unusually significant until he came to a point where the moccasins swung back to the left. The bear still followed — and David's heart gave a sudden thump! At first it

74 WildLife?

might have been coincidence, a bit of chance. It was chance no longer. It was deliberate. The claws were on the trail of the moccasins. David halted and pocketed his pipe, on which he had not drawn a breath in several minutes. He looked at his rifle, making sure that it was ready for action. Baree was growling. His white fangs gleamed and lurid lights were in his eyes as he gazed ahead and sniffed. David shuddered. Without doubt the claws had overtaken the moccasins by this time.

It was a grizzly. He guessed that much by the size of the spoor. He followed it across a bar of gravel. Then they turned a twist in the creek and came to other sand. A cry of amazement burst from David's lips when he looked closely at the two trails again.

The moccasins were now following the grizzly!

He stared, for a few moments disbelieving his eyes. Here, too, there was no room for doubt. The feet of the Indian boy had trod in the tracks of the bear. The evidence was conclusive; the fact astonishing. Of course, it was barely possible —

Whatever the thought might have been that was in David's mind it never reached a conclusion. He did not cry out at what he saw after that. He made no sound. Perhaps he did not even breathe. But it was there — under his eyes; inexplicable, amazing, not to be easily believed. A third time the order of the mysterious footprints in the sand was changed — and the grizzly was now following the boy, obliterating almost entirely the indentures in the sand of his small, moccasined feet. He wondered if it was possible that his eyes had gone bad on him, or that his mind had slipped out of its normal groove and was tricking him with weirdly absurd hallucinations. So what happened in almost that same breath did not startle him as it might otherwise have done. It was for a brief moment simply another assurance of his insanity, and if the mountains had suddenly turned over and balanced themselves on their peaks their gymnastics would not have frozen him into a more speechless stupidity than the girl who rose before him just then, not twenty paces away. She had appeared like an apparition from behind a great boulder — a little older, a little taller, a bit wilder than she had seemed to him in the picture, but with that same glorious hair sweeping about her, and that same questioning look in her eyes as she stared at him. Her hands were in that same way at her side, too, as if she was on the point of running away from him. He tried to speak. He believed, afterward, that he even made an effort to hold out his arms. But he was powerless. And so they stood there, twenty paces apart, staring as if they had met from the ends of the earth. Something happened then to whip David's reason back into its place. He heard a crunching, heavy, slow. From around the other end of the boulder came a huge bear. A monster. Ten feet from the girl. The first cry rushed out of his throat. It was a warning, and in the same instant he flung his rifle to his shoulder. The girl was quicker than he — like an arrow, a flash, a whirlwind of burnished tresses as she flew to the side of the great beast. She stood with her back against it, her two hands clutching its tawny hair, her slim body quivering, her eyes flashing at David. He felt weak. He lowered his rifle and advanced a few steps.

"Who — what — " he managed to say, and stopped. He was powerless to go on. But she seemed to understand. Her body stiffened.

"I am Marge O'Doone," she said defiantly. "And this is my bear!"

Grizzly Boy
Nancy Cooper

Ten-year-old Shane Miller spends each summer with his parents and his younger sister, Shannon, in a small log cabin high in the mountains of the Northwest Territories. His father, Sam, is a wildlife biologist studying mountain grizzlies for the N.W.T. government. There are no roads leading to the beautiful, wild valley where the Millers live — people, mail and supplies are flown in by chartered plane from the small town of Norman Wells. Shane loves the long summer days of the Canadian north and over the past five years has met many of the animals that also live in the valley. Here's the story of how he met the largest grizzly he's ever seen . . .

Shane heard a noise in the sky and looked out the window of his family's log cabin. He was excited because he knew exactly what it meant. The noise grew louder and louder until a tiny black dot appeared on the horizon over the mountain valley.

"Hey, Dennis is coming in the chopper," Shane yelled to his sister Shannon, and together they raced down the hill to where Dennis, the pilot, was already easing his Bell 47 helicopter down among some scrubby northern willows.

"I spotted a grizzly down by the Ekwi River!" Dennis shouted over the roar of the dying helicopter engine. "Go tell Sam!" But Shane was already gone, running like the wind to his father. They'd been waiting three weeks now for this sighting so *he* was going to be the one to break the great news.

Sam and his assistant, Norm, quickly gathered together all the gear they'd need. They told Shane to get the pilot to start the engines again. There was no time to lose; it wasn't every day a grizzly came by.

Shane watched the loading operation; he wanted to help and wanted desperately to go with them, but didn't want to get in the way. Soon everything they needed for tagging the bear — pliers, ropes, scales and plastic ear tags — was loaded.

Just as they were ready to go Sam must have read the look on Shane's face, because before closing the helicopter door he said, "Do you want to come along this time?"

"Do I!"

"Okay, I'll go first and sedate the bear, then Dennis will fly back for you."

As Shane waited for Dennis to return, he imagined what was happening to the bear because he had seen his father sedate a bear before. Dennis would bring the helicopter down until it was hovering over the bear, then Sam would take careful aim with a special dart gun filled with a drug that would quieten the grizzly down long enough for someone to get near it and tag it.

Shane was impatient for Dennis to come back but he didn't have long to wait. Soon he was clambering up the steps into the helicopter, then they were off. Up, up, over the cabin they rose, straight up above the trees and across the nearby lake. Shane looked down between his feet to the ground far below and spotted the fort he and his sister had built in the bush. An alarmed family of mallard ducks took to the air, leaving a splashy trail on the water. The two mountain peaks they flew between were still covered with snow, even though it was July. It never gets very warm this far north; in fact, Shane wears his ski jacket while kids in the south are probably in their swimsuits.

Soon Shane spotted his father standing beside an enormous grizzly, looking into its mouth! The bear was awake, but because of the drug was unable to move. The chopper landed and Shane leaped out, remembering to duck his head as he ran out from under the still-spinning blades.

Sam and Norm were working fast. There was lots to do in a short time, because it's not wise to be too close to a grizzly once the effect of the drug wears off.

Norm pulled apart the grizzly's thick lips and looked carefully at its long, gleaming teeth. It's possible to tell how old a bear is from its teeth, so Norm expertly removed a small premolar with a pair of tooth pliers. Then Sam clipped two small plastic identification tags to the grizzly's ears.

"What shall we call him?" Sam asked.

"He's pretty big. How about Brute?" offered Shane. Norm and Sam then took their special animal scales and weighed Brute. He lived up to his name all right — more than 270 kilograms!

Two things still had to be done before the bear became active. Norman lifted Brute's head up while Sam strapped a thick radio collar around the animal's massive neck. The collar, loose enough so it wouldn't hurt the bear, would send out a radio signal that Sam could pick up in the helicopter. In this way he could easily track Brute during the summer months and find out how far he roamed in search of food before hibernating for the long Arctic winter.

Working very quickly now, because Brute was showing signs that the drug was beginning to wear off, Sam and Dennis loaded their equipment into the helicopter while Norm took Brute's picture. Shane breathed a big sigh of relief when they were all safely back in the helicopter and were able to watch Brute shamble off into the spruce forests, none the worse for his experience except for a small gap in his teeth.

Back in the cabin that night everybody had something to say about the day's adventure. Brute was the twenty-eighth bear that Sam had tagged in his five years in the mountains. His work for the Northwest Territories government provides valuable information about what these mountain grizzlies eat, how long they live and where, how many live in the area and how many get shot by hunters. This information allows the government to make sure that the bears continue to thrive in their wilderness home.

The sun stays up until 11 p.m. this far north. But that night Shane lay awake long after sunset thinking about the bear. What a story he'd have to tell his friends!

What Is Grizzly Country?

Andy Russell

It was very early in the morning in mid-June. The stars were gone, except Venus, and night shadows lingered restively in the deeper folds among the hills and mountains. The air was cool and still, smelling of new grass, wild geraniums, and the golden blooms of Indian turnip, where the prairies sweep in close before soaring up to the saw-toothed eagle aeries along the sky.

The horse carried his head low, threading the winding trail at a fast running walk on a loose rein. Having bucked the kinks out of his frame and mine back at the corral gate a half hour earlier, he was now tending to business, his ears working to pick up the bells of the pack string scheduled to leave on the first trip of the season across the Rockies to the wilds of the Flathead River in British Columbia. He did no more than cock an ear at four big mule deer bucks, their stubs of new antlers sheathed in velvet, bounding up out of a draw in the long springy leaps so typical of their kind. When I reined him after them to the top of a lookout butte not far from Indian Springs, the red sun was just breaking over the rim of the plains to the east. On the crest the horse stopped of his own will. We stood motionless, facing the sun with only a light zephyr of wind fingering his mane and the fringes of my buckskin jacket, as we watched the new day being born.

This is something of nature's witchery, when the night goes and the day comes to the living world. Nothing matches the back of a good horse as a place to watch it. No other place but here at the foot of the Rockies, where the prairies and the mountains meet, can its awesome and beautiful display be seen and felt so well. Only on a June morning, between the last of spring and the first of summer, does it impart such a feeling of sudden-bursting life. Here the Rockies are its great backdrop, a timber-topped ridge winging it to the north and the sprawling peaks of the Great Lewis Overthrust walling it off to the south. Mountain meadows, lakes, and ageless stone couple into solid magnificence. It is a marriage of light and life, a promise and a fulfillment of that promise. While the mountains light up at first sun in deep rose, swiftly changing to gold, and all shot through with deep purple shadow, it is as though the whole universe pauses for a long, heart-stretching moment, locked in a spell of deep wonder.

Not a sound broke the stillness that morning. The horse and I stood waiting, breathless. Then he gave a long sigh; the saddle creaked under me, and a spur rowel jingled. A meadow lark burst into song and was joined by a white-crowned sparrow and a solitaire. The spell was broken. The day and the whole country jumped into wakefulness, vital and alive.

No wonder the old Plains Indians worshipped the sun, for it is the root of all life. They too were aware of this moment in the morning and made a ritual of viewing it from the brow of a hill. The sun was a simple explanation of their existence, their promise of tomorrow and their reassurance of today. For some reason wild animals also sometimes stand motionless at dawn, as though listening to the first soft music of the waking day — caught in the magic. It is a thing to ponder.

The horse lifted his head, pointing his ears at a ridge between us and the sun. Like a reincarnation of the past when black hordes covered the plains, a long line of buffalo broke from a hidden fold to feed along its crest. The big animals were shaggy in half-shed winter coats. To the south a half dozen cow elk, sleek and saddle brown in their new summer coats, came trotting out of a draw and fanned out to drink at a little lake. They were perfectly reflected in its mirror surface, until the calves suddenly came gamboling through the shallows, shattering their mothers' images. Above and farther to the right, high on the face of the mountain, white rump patches heliographed the presence of a bunch of feeding bighorn rams. Still higher a golden eagle suddenly dropped from the point of a pinnacle, plummeting down for a low level pass over the grasslands in search of a ground squirrel for breakfast.

The horse swung his head sharply to the north as a musical jingle of Swiss bells gave the other horses away. They were standing on a small bench watching something above them.

Out of a patch of aspens came a big she-grizzly with two small cubs at heel. The sun glinted on her bright silver ruff and shoulder mantle and bounced off the coats of the two small replicas bounding ecstatically behind her.

Here was the living symbol of the mountain wilderness, one giving an impression of power and royalty matched by no other. She seemed to go slowly with a certain massiveness; yet she moved with smooth grace, covering the ground with surprising speed. She stopped to investigate something, and through my glasses I saw the flash of ivory-white claws as she pawed up a bit of sod. One or the other of the cubs trailing her would discover something of fascinating interest, whereupon they would poke small inquisitive snouts into a clump of grass or flowers. Then they would gallop to catch up, carefree and happy, yet disciplined and careful not to lose sight of their big mother for a moment. Apparently she had no particular destination in mind, though she traveled steadily, angling up toward a saddle where the ridge butted into the mountain.

She had the bearing of a monarch. In the old days, when unbroken wilderness stretched from here to Lake Winnipeg and the Mississippi Valley, the grizzly's kingdom was as vast as that wilderness. The grizzly was then king of all animals across the thousands of miles of his range. The big bears ate berries and buffalo meat along the Saskatchewan, the Missouri, and the Yellowstone. They wandered the country drained by the Colorado and the Rio Grande. They fed on the pine nuts and oak mast in the sierras of Arizona, Nevada, New Mexico, old Mexico, and California. They caught salmon in the tributaries of the Snake and the Columbia. They ranged from the parched mountains of the south to the frozen, barren prairies of the Arctic, from the Midwest to the beaches of the Pacific Ocean.

But when the white men came to plow the sod and kill the buffalo, this wilderness largely disappeared forever. The grizzly range shrank as the big animals were harried and decimated, running for the first time from any animal, the only one ever to challenge them successfully in their environment. More cautious and much less numerous, those that remained forted up in the mountain fastnesses of the west and north, never to venture far out into the plains again.

This was the edge of the wilderness, where I sat my horse, comparatively untouched by man save for the fence built as a sort of repentant afterthought to enclose the buffalo. Because it is wilderness protected within the boundaries of Waterton Lakes National Park, this southwest corner of Alberta is still grizzly country, and always will be grizzly country if the principles of national parks are guarded well.

Watching the mother grizzly top out on the saddle, it was evident that the female knew where safe haven lay; for had she traveled as many minutes in the opposite direction, she would have been in ranching country. There she would not be welcome, and her appearance would likely spark someone to shoot first and ask questions afterward.

But there is plenty of grizzly country in the mountains – – country that is high, wild, and rugged, a place where birds and streams and wind still blend in a song of the wilderness that lifts and falls in a cadence of freedom as sweet as life and as old as time among the proud gnarled trees and the rocky pinnacles.

That same wind blows across the plains to the east; the same waters flow down the valleys there, and the birds still nest and sing in the coverts. But there the song of freedom is muted now. It is not grizzly country any more. It is man country. The grizzly I watched knew it, and she was teaching her cubs by following the sun back into the wild fastnesses among the peaks.

Out on the Deep, Soft Snow

James Simpson

Have you ever kicked loose the sodden snowshoes and dropped wearily on the warm hillside to scan the country below through glasses for tracks of the early bear? Have you bathed in the warm sunshine and watched the soaring eagle wheel like a flash as he hears the cackle of ptarmigan seeking shelter in a rockslide? Have you seen him swoop with a hissing noise to the spot where he thinks the bird to be, in the hope, perhaps, that it will take frightened wing to a safer place? Have you seen it repeat in various places, then sail away to hunt game less sophisticated, until it becomes a faint, dark spot in the deepening blue of waning day? Have you turned again to your scrutiny and felt a thrill as a large, shambling, plunging spot crosses a deep snow gully and blends with the dead brown of the hillside below you?

It is a grizzly just renewing animal life after six months of hibernation in some dark cranny or upturned tree root and it is for that you have made the heart-breaking trip under adverse conditions, carrying a pack and sleeping without tent or sufficient bedding to keep waking often to replenish the log fire to proportions necessary to kill the chill of the frosty night.

Life's Finest Thrills

Have you wakened when the stars are paling and listened to the song of the white-crowned sparrow, who never seems to sleep? Have you watched the soft early light appear, felt the "pull" of the sleeping bag, the silence, the mystery and the joy of the new spring day? Have you watched the rose tints of the rising sun swell, turn paler; heard the song of the robin, the music of the brook, faint music during the frozen night but soon to swell to a sullen roar as the snows melt in the midday sun? Have you done this and not felt rather ashamed that your mission is one of death?

Have you cooked your frugal breakfast, noting the while the long line of trailing smoke from your all-night campfire lying low over the river as if held there by an unseen hand until it thins and vanishes in the blue of the distant hillside; felt the crunch of the frozen snow crust under the shoepacks that sounds like sugar on an oiled floor, and the nip of the morning air that stirs the blood as the sun bursts over the mountain flooding the valley with a golden light? That is bear hunting in the early spring and those who have not done it have missed much in life. Those are the things one looks back on, never forgets, and seldom repeats. Why? The car, the cushioned chair, the soft bed and the good things of life make us more artificial than real, even at the expense of health.

May, in Early Morn

Visualise this: A clear, cold morning in early May, with the first rays of the sun bursting on the higher peaks. Snow frozen hard enough to dispense with the snowshoes, but before long it will soften and travel for the day will be over. The sun peeps through a break in the ranges and floods the valley with a soft, warm light, but the open water of a clear spring creek calls a halt to look for a crossing, dry shod. A fallen log forms a bridge, but before it can be reached the willows part and a large grizzly walks into the open. He shakes himself and you see over the rifle sights the sheen of his long, silky coat. The wind is right and he has not seen you, but as the discharge echoes and re-echoes it does not drown the savage roar of the stricken animal. He plunges head-long toward you unconscious of your presence, but of that you are not aware. Something tickles up and down your spine and your very hair roots fill with motion. You hear him splash in the open creek and stand, every muscle tense, awaiting his reappearance. It seems like hours — it is but seconds. Then you see him lying motionless in the clear cold water, a trailing line of crimson winding slowly past. Gingerly you approach, but there is no need for care, only strength, strength to pull the huge bulk to the gravel beach, where the final chapter may be written with the hunting knife. And through it all the robins sing and the chipmunks play, oblivious that another tragedy in their world of tragedies has happened.

That is a fair sample of a spring bear hunt. It may sound hard. It is. It may sound foolish, but is it? It has its compensations and its pleasures. Were life-giving health the sole reward it would be full of worth, but the memories that will never fade are yours and yours alone.

Still Shots Echo
Ken Belford

Still shots echo in a deliberate land,
Almost daring me
To go too far into it.

I've squinted down gun barrels here,
And closed the other eye
When I squeezed the trigger.

There's an abnormal fusion at the other ends of my sight.
And the poles I've believed in 'till now
Come turning back upon themselves.

But I hunt the Arctic grouse.
Tho always I know that to another kind of eye,
There might be nothing here.

A small grey circle of smoke drifts away from me.
A cigarette drops at my feet.
Cold fingertips meet melt and stick to colder steel.

Hit. The startled bird lifts its already dying body
And clumsily drifts across the river
To die on the other side. No one can cross here.

There is no prize today
And a deeper silence. No echo now.
And I wonder if a law has been broken,

Feeling that I've shot more than a bird
Hung out there
At the end of a dry limb.

Search by Air

Max Braithwaite

Wilf Gardner was doing something he'd wanted to do ever since he was a boy. He was flying over Northern Alberta in a small aircraft.

But he had never thought he would do it this way, searching for his children and their friend.

Now, as he sat beside his wife and looked down on the maze of lakes and vegetation below, he realized what an immense land it was. Looking for three small people down there was worse than searching for a snowflake in a blizzard.

He shifted his glance nervously to the brown leather jacket of the pilot and the red coat of the Mountie in the seats in front of him.

Beside her husband Meg Gardner sat thin-lipped and silent. Of course the children are all right, she told herself again and again. That's the way we've raised them — to be able to take care of themselves. They simply crawled under their canoe during the storm and spent the night.

But as she thought back over what had happened during the past twenty hours, she couldn't help feeling sick with worry.

The worry had really begun when they'd finally managed to row the heavy motorboat across the lake to the spot where they had left their stationwagon. "Yoohoo, kids! We're back," she'd shouted when they got near shore.

But there'd been no answer, and no sign of the canoe.

That was when she'd got the first real stab of fear. It had increased when they'd rushed up the beach, just ahead of the storm, and got into the stationwagon for protection. Still there was no sign of the kids.

"They'll be all right," Wilf Gardner had told her for the tenth time. "After all, what could happen to them? They've been out in worse storms than this before." But he didn't sound as though he believed a word of it.

The worst of the storm had passed to the north of them but, even so, the wind was near gale force. As they sat watching the whitecaps on the lake, a truck had pulled up near them.

A man in khaki shirt and slacks got out and came over to their car.

"I'm Orville Tyhurst of the Provincial Forestry Service," he said. "Pardon me for asking, but what are you people doing away up here, and how did you find this place?"

"Oh, I'm so glad you've come," Meg Gardner exploded, ignoring the question. "We've lost our children!"

"What?"

"Uh, she doesn't mean it exactly that way," Wilf Gardner explained. "They went across the lake with us and they haven't returned."

Orville Tyhurst looked confused. "Across the lake! There's nothing over there but the worst tangle of bush you ever saw."

"They didn't exactly stay there. They went down a river . . ."

"And we went down another," Meg Gardner cut in. "When we came back to the meeting-place, they weren't there. We thought they'd come back here, but they hadn't. And now this storm. . . ."

From the way she wet her lips with the tip of her tongue and stared at him for reassurance, Orville Tyhurst could tell this woman was worried. Tourists, he thought. Why can't they stay in the regular campgrounds? Aloud, he asked, "When did all this happen?"

"We left here this morning, quite early."

"Um hm." Orville Tyhurst looked out over the stormy lake. The sun had gone down and it was getting dark quickly. That country beyond the lake was the worst in the area. Nobody went in there. But he wasn't going to tell these people that.

"Ma'am," he said carefully, "there's nothing we can do tonight."

"But we've got to do something," Meg Gardner insisted. "You don't understand. Oh, I wish Jeff had never heard of whooping cranes!"

"Whooping cranes!" Orville Tyhurst said.

Meg Gardner was so upset that she wasn't making much sense. "And those awful men who've been following us!" she went on, close to tears.

Orville Tyhurst stared in amazement. Before he could speak, Wilf Gardner interjected, "It's a long story, Mr. Tyhurst. I guess I'd better begin at the beginning."

Then he told it all: the car that followed them, the prowler, slashed tire, hitchhiker, theft of the map — right up until the time when the youngsters had left on their own.

Orville Tyhurst pushed his cap back on his head. "Well, I'll be a budworm's uncle. It just happens that there is a big valley north of here, a valley nobody ever goes near much. It's treacherous even to fly over — mostly marsh."

"There is a valley!" Wilf Gardner exclaimed. "Could the kids get into it? I mean, from that river?"

The Forestry man thought for a minute. "I'm not sure. As I say, that's mean country. But we can certainly have a look at it first thing tomorrow morning." He began walking towards the truck. "I'll use my truck radio to contact the RCMP detachment at Fort McMurray. My guess is they'll have a plane here shortly after daylight.''

The plane had landed on the lake soon after dawn, and had taxied in to shore. The Mountie, Sergeant Fournier, had listened to their story without comment.

"I think we'd better get up there right away," he'd said then, glancing skyward. "According to the forecast, this weather isn't going to improve."

They had taken off at once.

Now the pilot half turned in his seat towards them and pointed down through the clouds. "That the place you left them?" he asked.

Wilf Gardner looked carefully. It was hard to tell from the air, but it looked like it. There was the weedy shore, and there were the mouths of two small rivers.

"I think so," he shouted.

"Okay," the pilot shouted back. "I'm going to take a pass at it. Keep your eyes open."

He banked steeply, losing altitude as he did so, swung around in a big arc and came in low over the shore. But, being unused to sighting things from the air, Wilf and Meg Gardner weren't much help. Every stump and log looked as though it might be a person. And it all flashed past so quickly that they couldn't tell.

When they had again gone into the low-hanging clouds, the pilot looked back at them quizzically. They both shrugged helplessly and shook their heads.

"I'll try again," he shouted, and made another run over the shore. This time they were able to see more. But there was no sign of the children.

As the plane gained altitude once more, it hit an air pocket that dropped it about fourteen feet straight down.

"She's pretty rough this morning," the pilot commented calmly. "Turbulence after the storm. There's another much bigger lake just north of here that they could easily have got into," he added.

Now Wilf and Meg Gardner couldn't see anything but greyness on both sides. For all they could tell, the aircraft might have been flying upside down.

Then they came out of the cloud and saw the water, grey and forbidding below them. It was absolutely empty. Even the ducks weren't showing themselves.

The pilot flew the full length of the lake. It was long and narrow and bent like a horseshoe. As they neared the southeast end, the Mountie shouted something to the pilot, who nodded and brought the plane in really low, just above the trees. Wilf Gardner could make out a logging road leading up to a crude landing in the lake. That would be the road that had branched off the one they'd driven in on, he thought.

"There! Down there . . . look!" Meg Gardner shouted, pointing down.

"What did you see?" the Mountie asked, as the plane banked for a turn.

"Something shiny in the trees. I just caught a glimpse of it. Black and shiny, like a car!"

The plane came in low again. This time they all saw it, a long, black car off the side of the trail in the bushes.

"That looks like the car!" Wilf Gardner shouted. "The one that was passing us all the way up here."

"So, we know the men are here, at least," Sergeant Fournier said grimly. "And if there are whoopers in this area and they molest the birds, they'll be in serious trouble. Whoopers are protected by federal law. Now let's see if we can spot the kids."

The plane banked into a turn and flew low the full length of the lake, along the opposite shore. They saw nothing. Then the plane climbed into the clouds again, and the Gardners caught only scattered glimpses of the lakes and trees below.

Again the pilot leaned back, half turning in his seat, and

spoke to his passengers. He pointed a finger towards the north. "The valley is in that direction, but we don't often fly over it. The sides are so steep that you get a treacherous updraught. Then in the middle there's the worst down-draught you ever saw."

"How does anybody get into it?" Wilf Gardner asked.

"They don't. Not from this end. I think there's an opening where the river runs out of it way down at the other end. But, as far as I know, nobody goes in there except maybe the odd Indian trapper."

Meg Gardner leaned forward and raised her voice. "Perhaps the children found a way in."

The pilot shook his head. "Don't see how they could have. There's a small river runs out of Horseshoe Lake into the valley, but it drops off the escarpment. Nobody could go over that waterfall in a canoe."

Wilf Gardner tapped the pilot on the shoulder. "Jeff may have tried it," he said. "Especially if he saw a whooping crane. You can't know how crazy that kid is for birds. Once he climbed a fifty-foot poplar to rescue some abandoned baby owls, and got his face scratched for his pains."

"One thing's certain," the pilot admitted. "They're not out here on Horseshoe Lake." He gestured helplessly. "It'd be bad enough flying into that valley in clear weather, but in this peasoup it's going to be really tough."

"There isn't much else we can do," Sergeant Fournier said.

"I know, I know. Updraught or no updraught, we've got to chance it. It's going to be rough, folks, so hang onto your seats."

The plane banked sharply and turned north.

"Are you all right? Are you shot?" Eagle Eye hissed as Jeff fell in front of him in the canoe.

"No, of course I'm not shot," Jeff whispered, pulling himself up. "His gun went off in the air. We took him by surprise. It was you shooting forward like that that knocked me off balance!''

"Well, I'm sorry. I thought for sure he was going to shoot you," the Indian boy said. "I had to move fast to spoil his aim. Now keep your head down. Our only hope is not to let them see us again."

Jeff got onto his knees, grabbed his paddle and pushed with all his might at the side of the narrow channel, keeping his head low, as Eagle Eye had instructed.

High above, the healthy whooper circled in the sky, unwilling to leave its mate.

The canoe couldn't go very fast along the narrow, winding channel. Jeff knew that in the inlet the men would be making better time.

"Krawk! Krawk!"

It was the sound of the young whooper somewhere ahead. Then there was another sound: the pitiful squawking of the wounded bird.

Then came the sound of more shouting from the men. "They know the bird is hurt!" Eagle Eye exclaimed. "So they are not being quiet any more."

The squawking and the shouting increased.

"Out of the canoe!" Eagle Eye commanded. "The channel turns here. They will see us if we go down it."

Jeff stepped out of the canoe onto the soggy ground, sinking up to his ankles in ooze.

Moving as quickly as he could, he followed Eagle Eye through the high reeds. Suddenly the Indian boy stopped and motioned to him. Jeff crept cautiously up behind him and peered over his shoulder.

They were on the edge of the inlet, just barely screened from view by the rushes. About two hundred feet across the water, on the other side of the inlet, was the whooping crane's nest. In the water beside it was the brown rubber raft, now completely bare of the brush that had camouflaged it.

Beside the raft were two men. The big man, the hitchhiker, was holding the high-powered rifle and gazing around at the rushes, apparently searching for them. The other, a much shorter, thinner man with a sharp face, held the ends of a fishnet which he had thrown over the injured crane and its youngster. He was pulling the drawstrings of the net tight.

Jeff swallowed hard. Here were two of the most precious birds in the world held captive: one-sixteenth of the world's total population of whooping cranes!

A low noise beside him made him turn. Eagle Eye was gazing at the scene with a look of concentrated hatred. His lips were drawn in a straight line and a muscle at the corner of his jaw twitched.

Beside the Indian boy's, Jeff's anger was nothing. Eagle Eye was watching an age-old story all over again: the life of the wilderness being destroyed by the ruthless skill of the white man.

"What can we do?" Jeff whispered.

Eagle Eye didn't answer. Quickly he looked among the reeds and selected a long, hollow stem. He broke it off to a length of about eighteen inches.

Then he drew his long, sharp knife from its sheath and held it in his right hand. Holding the reed with his left hand and placing one end in his mouth, he slipped into the water.

Jeff had seen pictures of this. It was a trick used by some Indians for hunting ducks. The hollow reed provided a breathing tube which would enable Eagle Eye to swim underwater and approach the raft unseen. If he could slash a hole in the bottom of the raft and let the air out the two men would be stranded in the marsh. It was a wild, reckless thing to try, Jeff realized. But he knew that the Indian boy would take any chance, no matter how hopeless, to try to save the birds — his tribe's guardian spirits.

Jeff crouched low and watched the tip of the tiny reed moving across the water. The man with the rifle was still peering around at the rushes, looking as if he were ready to shoot anything that moved.

Jeff held his breath. Would he see that moving reed?

Then Jeff heard the other man speak: "Let's get these birds loaded on the raft and get back to the boat. Those fool kids are around here somewhere. Lord knows what they'll be up to."

"They won't be up to nothing; not while I'm watching!" the other said. "I'd sure like to get another shot at that other bird, too."

"Too late for that," the other growled. "Let's get out of here."

"Okay," the big one agreed. He pulled the rubber raft closer to shore and bent over to help drag the birds towards it.

The moving reed was within a dozen feet of the raft.

Suddenly the smaller man got back into the raft. "Watch this!" he shouted, "and keep your gun ready!"

His movement caused the raft to float close to the moving reed. Immediately, he reached out, grabbed it, and yanked it out of the water. Then he reached down into the water, came up with Eagle Eye's right wrist and dragged the rest of the boy up with it.

"Well, what do you know!" he sneered. "A real live Indian! Well, I guess nobody'll worry too much about what happens to you!" He twisted the boy's arm cruelly.

Eagle Eye didn't make a sound, but the knife dropped from his fingers.

The big man pointed his gun straight at Eagle Eye's head. "All right," he shouted across the water. "We know there's two of you. Now, the other one show yourself, or I'll let your friend have it!"

There was only one thing Jeff could do. He stood up among the reeds.

"All right, you," the short man shouted, turning to him. "Get around here fast. And don't try to run away or it will be

too bad for your redskin friend!'' The way he said ''redskin''
made it sound like a nasty word.

Jeff plodded around the edge of the inlet. Once he sank up
to his knees in the muck, but he managed to pull himself out
quickly.

When he finally got to the men, all he could look at was the
birds in the net. The adult bird was a crumpled heap of black
and white feathers. Its long neck was stretched against the
netting, its beak was open, and it was panting in the same way
Oscar, Jeff's pet crow, had panted when Jeff had first held him
in his hand. Its eyes were glazed with terror. One wing stood off
from the body at a crazy angle.

The young bird looked like a brown feather duster with
long, awkward legs and a long neck. It was squawking pitifully,
but otherwise seemed to be all right.

Jeff gulped helplessly. This might well be the only
whooping crane baby born this year, and here it was a helpless
captive. He knew it couldn't long survive this kind of rough
handling.

The big hitchhiker seized him by the shoulder and shoved
him over against Eagle Eye. The Indian boy didn't even look at
Jeff. It was almost as though he included him in his hatred.

''What are we going to do with them?'' the big man asked.
He looked hard at Jeff.

The other rubbed his bristly chin with a wide dirty hand.
''What's wrong with leaving them here? If we wreck their
canoe, we'll be miles from here before they find their way out.
They won't starve. The Indian will see to that.''

''Okay, let's get going then.'' The hitchhiker bent over to
pick up the birds, and then froze. ''What's that?''

The other listened a second. ''An aeroplane!'' he said.
''And coming this way!'' He didn't hesitate a second. ''Okay,
you two, on your bellies in those weeds. Flat. And don't
move!''

Each man grabbed a boy and threw him down among the

deep rushes. While the big man held them there, the smaller man grabbed the rubber boat and the birds and pulled them into cover. Then each man held one of the boys down in the muck, completely hidden by the rushes.

As the aeroplane flew towards the edge of the escarpment the pilot warned, "Hold on now, this is it."

Wilf and Meg Gardner clutched the arm rests of their seats, and just in time. The aircraft jostled heavily, its wings wagging dangerously. Then it settled again into level flight. "I'm going down as low as I can get," the pilot shouted. "Keep your eyes open now."

He banked steeply and came in as close to the waterfall as he could. The parents searched the ground hopefully for some sign of the children, while Sergeant Fournier looked for something else that he hoped he wouldn't see: a wrecked canoe.

No one saw anything.

The pilot brought the plane down to about four hundred feet and flew along the river towards the lake. "I don't dare go any lower," he shouted over his shoulder. "The downdraught might ditch us."

From this height the valley floor was seen as one huge, soggy mess. "If they're in here we'll sure be able to see them," the pilot said. But he had to admit to himself that he couldn't see why anyone would be in such a wasteland. He looked over to the right, where a thick growth of bush grew against the valley wall: no chance of getting very close to that, because of the updraught. Looking for people on the ground from an aeroplane, he mused, certainly wasn't the easy job most people thought it to be.

He decided to make one run along the whole length of the valley and then come back again. Then he'd look somewhere else.

When Mattie had heard the shot she had felt a terror such as she had never felt before: terror and helplessness. "We've got to help!'' she had cried out, but she knew that there was nothing they could do. She sank to the ground and began to cry.

Mutt began to say something and then realized that it was no use. He felt too much like crying himself. Leaving her alone, he went back to the boat. Maybe he could find a piece of wire that he could use for the ignition. He searched frantically but found none. Then he climbed a tree to see what he could see from there. He tore his pants, but saw nothing. The bush was too thick.

The only thing to do, he decided, was to try to take the canoe back over the lake. But without proper paddles that was all but impossible, too.

Then he heard a shout from Mattie. ''Mutt,'' she called. ''I heard something. I'm sure. It sounded like a motor.''

Mutt ran back to where she was sitting and they listened together. Away off they heard the roar of an aeroplane.

''It's coming this way,'' Mattie breathed, standing up. ''They must be looking for us!''

''They'll never see us,'' Mutt said. ''Not in this jungle.''

The roar of the plane became louder. It was obvious that it was flying down the valley.

''If they don't see us they'll go away!'' Mattie said urgently. ''Oh, what can we do?''

''Not a thing!'' Mutt stormed. ''Not a solitary, blasted thing. We're beat!''

''No! No, we're not!'' Mattie yelled. ''Didn't you say there was gasoline in that tank at the boat? We can light a fire!''

''Hey! That's an idea!'' Mutt said. He began running back to the boat, with Mattie slightly ahead of him.

''Listen!'' Mutt yelled. ''The plane's turning. It must be going back along the valley. We've got to get some smoke into the air before it leaves!''

They reached the boat together and, as Mutt heaved the heavy gas tank over the side onto the bank, Mattie began hauling the crates and loose pieces of lumber out after it.

"Make a tight pile," Mutt panted. "We don't want to start a bush fire here." He looked around at the trees, still dripping from the night's rain. Well, that was one good thing about this damp, cloudy day. There wasn't much chance of starting a fire accidentally.

The pile of lumber was getting bigger, but the noise of the plane was getting louder.

"Light it!" Mattie screamed. "Or they'll be gone!"

Mutt unscrewed the cap from the gas tank. Then, using all his strength, he heaved it up and poured the gas out onto the pile of wood. Now for a match. He fished in his pockets, took out the tin match box, and deliberately pried open the lid. Then he took out a match and scratched it. As it flared into flame, he tossed it towards the pile of gasoline-soaked crates and ducked back fast.

With a loud "pop" it burst into flames, and a black, greasy smoke went pouring up through the trees.

Jeff Gardner lay on his side in the bulrushes. Crouching at his side, the hitchhiker held him down so firmly that he could hardly even move his head. Beside him, Eagle Eye was getting even rougher treatment from the smaller man, who was kneeling on him, peering out through the weeds, holding the rifle ready.

In their net, the cranes squawked and squirmed helplessly.

The plane had passed over their heads and to the right. They could hear its motor far down the valley.

"Well?" the big man asked. "They didn't see us." He moved as though to stand up.

"Keep down, you fool!" the other hissed. "They'll be back for another look."

The hitchhiker quickly dropped back onto his knees.

Sure enough, the sound of the plane had changed and was getting louder again. But it was even farther to the right this time. There was no chance of them being seen.

Jeff felt sick. If the plane left, who would ever find them in this place? And the men would leave with the whooping cranes. Even if the men were caught, the big birds would never survive the treatment they were getting. It would mean two more whoopers gone from the world.

The roar of the plane dinned in his ears. Then suddenly its sound changed again. There was a loud splash on the lake. Had they crashed?

"They're down!" the small man reported from his vantage point. "Somebody lit a fire on the other side of the lake. The pilot must have seen it and he's landed!"

Mutt and Mattie! Jeff's heart leaped. It must be! Who else could have lighted a fire?

The hitchhicker was cursing a blue streak. "How are we going to get out of here with that plane snooping around?" he growled.

"Shut your big fat mouth!" the other commanded. "And keep down. Nobody's going to see us here!"

"What's the plane doing?" the big man wanted to know.

"Turning around to go back along the lake," the small man growled. "And if they do they'll find the boat. This calls for a well-placed bullet." Keeping one knee on Eagle Eye's back, he raised himself and lifted the rifle.

"What are you doing?" the big man protested. "We can't go shooting people. We're in enough trouble already with those kids we've got tied up."

"I'm not going to shoot anybody," the other man muttered. "But a slug in the engine will keep them sitting there on the lake and give us a chance to get back to our boat. It's the only chance we've got." He took aim.

Then things happened fast. With a loud squawking, Oscar the crow flapped in from nowhere and tried to land on Jeff's shoulder. On the way, his big wings brushed against the small man's face. With a cry of alarm, the man jerked back, his finger tightening on the trigger. The gun went off in the air.

With the pressure suddenly released from his back, Eagle Eye squirmed around like an eel, wound his arms about the man's legs and heaved.

The man fell with a squishy thud and the gun flew out of his hands. The hitchhiker left Jeff and sprang to help his partner and, as he did so, Jeff leaped up, grabbed the gun from among the reeds and pitched it out as far as he could into the marsh. Then he ran, splashing through the water and muck towards the plane. "Help!" he yelled, as he'd never yelled before. "Help!"

At the sound of the shot the pilot had looked towards them. Now, seeing the struggle, he revved his engine and steered towards shore. The door of the plane opened and a rifle was poked out. The arm that held it wore a red coat.

"All right," a steady voice shouted. "Everybody stay where they are and stop what they're doing!"

"Sure, we're safe enough now," Jeff Gardner said, "but what about the cranes? We've fixed them. But good! What hope is there for them now?"

He and Mattie and Mutt were sitting on canvas chairs in their camp on the shore of the lake. Mrs. Gardner was working in the big tent nearby.

It was four days after the dramatic rescue and Jeff still felt the thrill of the plane ride. The pilot had loaded the crooks, the kids, including Eagle Eye, and the two whoopers into the plane and flown them back to the Gardner camp. "I think some people interested in whooping cranes will want to ask this Indian boy some questions," Sergeant Fournier had said.

Then the Mountie had taken the crooks to Edmonton. Wilf Gardner had gone with them to give evidence. They had taken the injured whooper and young one to be cared for by Dr. Blythe.

Then had come an even bigger thrill for Jeff. The very next day Dr. Blythe had arrived at the camp in a Wild Life Service plane. He was a short, balding man with glasses and the keenest eyes Jeff had ever seen. It would be safe to say that right then he was the most excited bird man in North America.

"Whoopers!" he'd exclaimed. "And this far south. Of course, that's not surprising in itself. Years ago the birds nested farther south than this. But we thought they'd vanished from this area. We thought fear of man had driven them north of parallel sixty. Only the remoteness of the hidden valley can account for it."

And when he'd met Eagle Eye, Dr. Blythe's enthusiasm had known no bounds. "Imagine! The best bird men of two countries, with aircraft to help them, have been searching for years for whooping crane nesting-sites. And here you've been quietly watching them all the time, without even a pair of binoculars!" He'd pounded the Indian boy on the back and beamed.

But, to Jeff's surprise, Eagle Eye had not been pleased with his praise. He had merely nodded and listened intently to the rest of what Dr. Blythe had to say.

"So now we have a wounded female and a young whooper in captivity," the bird man had continued. "If we had the male it would give me a chance to test a theory of mine."

"What's that, sir?" Jeff had asked.

"Well, more and more I'm coming to believe that the only hope for these magnificent birds is for us to capture a family group and raise them in captivity. Their 2,500-mile migration flight during the spring and fall is just too dangerous for the dwindling flock. A bad storm could wipe them all out."

"Oh, I know," he'd continued, noticing the look on Jeff's face, "most wild creatures are better off in their natural habitat, but the whooping crane is a special case. We've got to do something drastic. There's only one hitch, of course. We don't have the male bird. And, for the life of me, I know of no way to catch him."

This had only served to make Jeff feel bad all over again

about having led the crooks to the whoopers. The family of birds had been broken up, and would never be together again. He had felt even worse when, later that day, Eagle Eye had disappeared from the camp without even saying goodbye.

"Will he get home all right?" he'd asked his mother.

"I'm sure of it, Jeff. He probably knows a way through the bush south of Horseshoe Lake and through the canyon. Travelling on foot is nothing new to him."

But Jeff had still felt bad. He had become very fond of the Indian boy and had hoped that Eagle Eye might accept him as a friend, even though he was white. But it was evidently not to be.

Dr. Blythe spent most of his time cautiously studying the country over towards the hidden valley, looking for evidence of any more whooping cranes. Jeff had gone with him the first day, but this particular morning he had gone by himself, leaving very early.

Now Jeff sighed heavily. "The worst part of it is, it's all my fault," he said. "Instead of helping the whoopers, I helped those crooks find them. Now this nesting-site is gone. The male will never mate again."

"Easy there, boy," Mutt said, taking another bite of his apple. Since getting back to camp he'd hardly stopped eating. "It wasn't your fault."

"Of course not," Mattie agreed. "Don't forget, that storm would have injured the female anyway and if we hadn't been there she'd have died. Now she's safe in a pen with her broken wing in a splint and her young one with her."

Mrs. Gardner came out of the tent and looked at the three adventurers. "I could use some help," she said good-naturedly. "Your father and Sergeant Fournier will be landing on the lake any time now and I want to have lunch ready for them."

When the Mountie's plane taxied in towards their camp the youngsters were waiting with a dozen questions.

"Their names are Bill Hargan and Joe Leach," Sergeant

Fournier said. "Joe is the small one and the brains of the corporation. They're both experienced woodsmen; they've trapped and hunted through parts of northern Canada for years. In the past few years they've made a good deal of money supplying specimens to a Mr. Angus McGilvary, a millionaire who lives in the Bahamas."

"Specimens!" Jeff snorted disgustedly.

"Yes," Wilf Gardner said. "Those two became quite expert at catching birds alive. It seems this McGilvary has one of the greatest collections of live and stuffed birds in the world. But he hasn't got a whooping crane and he'd give a small fortune to get one."

"Like ten thousand dollars," Mutt said.

"Well, he didn't offer that much at first. Hargan and Leach had a standing order to supply a whooping crane, but McGilvary had never offered ten thousand dollars," Mr. Gardner explained. "They knew that getting one out of Wood Buffalo Park was next to impossible. In the first place the park is supervised, with no hunting allowed, and in the second place the nesting-sites there are so hard to get at that nobody but Dr. Blythe and one other person have ever been close to them. And they had helicopters and the co-operation of the Wild Life Service."

"Hargan and Leach could hardly expect that," Mattie commented.

"No," Sergeant Fournier smiled, "but believe it or not, they were going to try to get a whooper from Wood Buffalo, just the same. They'd organized their equipment, including that big rubber raft with the electric motor, and they were just about set to go when they happened to see Jeff on television."

Jeff winced. "Me and my big mouth. I gave the whole show away."

"Note quite," his father said. "They still didn't know where the actual place you were talking about was. They tried to find out by means of the phone call, which you didn't tell us about until afterwards.'' He looked hard at Jeff. ''And then, when that didn't work, they decided to follow us and steal the letter and map. They knew your name from the television program, so it was easy for them to find our address, and you had mentioned that we were leaving next morning.''

''But first they wired McGilvary in the Bahamas asking for more money. Since they had to follow us and couldn't wait in Calgary for the answer, they instructed him to wire his reply to the telegraph office in Edmonton.''

''That's why they slashed our tire!'' Mattie exclaimed. ''Of course! Don't you see? They had to delay us long enough to go back to Edmonton to get that reply.''

''Right,'' Wilf Gardner said. ''If Hargan — he was the prowler — had found the map and letter in the tent that first night, they wouldn't have had to follow us. When he failed, he had to delay us by slashing the tire, and then he tried the hitchhiking stunt to try to find out where we were going. That failed too, so they tried to steal the map again, and this time they succeeded.''

''You know, it's funny,'' Mutt said. ''The map couldn't have been much help to them in finding the spot anyway. It gave just the general location.''

''But the letter was invaluable,'' Wilf Gardner said. ''Leach became quite talkative and he admitted that they'd been in the Horseshoe Lake area before, but of course never in Hidden Valley. So they recognized Horseshoe Lake from the letter.''

''And when we saw them in Horseshoe, they weren't looking for us at all, but for the river that leads into the valley. Is that it?'' Mutt asked.

''Yes,'' the Mountie said. ''And they found it. The entrance to it is well hidden by bulrushes and willows. It doesn't fall off the escarpment like the one you kids were on. It runs through a deep, narrow gorge the water has worn through the soft sandstone. It's almost like a tunnel. There's really only one bad set of rapids on it, and those two were able to carry their boat and motor and other gear round that. Then, when the river gets to the valley, it runs through that area of the deep bush. It was a perfect place to hide their camp and boat.''

''And we'd never have found it if the storm hadn't blown our canoe across the lake,'' Mattie said.

''It seems they'd set out on their bird-hunting expedition before the storm and then had to turn back,'' Wilf Gardner said. ''That's when they surprised Mutt and Mattie.''

Mattie shuddered. ''They sure tie hard knots.''

Sergeant Fournier's jaw was firm. ''Yes, but I don't think they'll do a thing like that again. It practically amounts to kidnapping, and that carries a very stiff penalty.''

''They were very ingenious men in their own evil way,'' Meg Gardner said quietly.

''They were that,'' her husband agreed. ''And they were prepared to float around for days, if necessary, to get close enough to the nest to capture the birds. But of course the kids spoiled that.''

''So you see, Jeff, you did save the whoopers,'' Mattie said. ''At least you and Eagle Eye did.''

The mention of the Indian boy made Jeff sad again.

Dr. Blythe came back at seven. ''I'm afraid it's not much use, Jeff,'' he said. ''I followed your route as far as the waterfall, and spent hours there with my binoculars trained on the nest site. But there's no sign of the male bird. I'm afraid he's completely abandoned the nest, perhaps flown north. At any rate, he's lost, as far as helping to increase the flock is concerned. He'll never mate again.''

Then to everybody's surprise, a sound, now familiar to the youngsters, rang out over the lake.

''Kerloo-ker-lee-loo!''

''The whooper!'' Jeff gasped, and ran like a deer towards the shore. The others followed. But what they saw was not the great white bird. A large canoe with three figures in it, towing a small red canoe, was rapidly approaching the shore.

They watched in amazement as the canoe came to the beach and grated on the sand.

"Eagle Eye!" Jeff yelled, recognizing the centre figure.

The Indian boy came up the beach and stood very straight in front of Jeff. "This is my father, Swift Moccasin, and my uncle, Standing Bear," he said formally. "We have brought something."

As those on the beach stared in disbelief, the two Indians gently lifted a large white form from the bottom of the red canoe. It was the male whooping crane, legs and wings securely bound with soft cloth so that it should not hurt itself. They laid it on the sand.

"We knew it must be with its family, wherever they are," Swift Moccasin said simply.

The Indians explained what had happened. Being experts at snaring birds and game, they had gone to the nesting-area at night, set their snares, and lain in hiding. Eagle Eye, who could imitate the whooper's call perfectly, had called the big bird in and they had caught it.

"Then it was you we heard calling just now," Jeff said.

Eagle Eye nodded.

"We knew that the giant birds would leave the valley now and never come back," Swift Moccasin explained. "From what Eagle Eye told us, we thought it would be best to bring the male bird here."

"But what about the guardian spirit thing, and you having to leave the valley if the birds do?" Jeff asked.

Swift Moccasin dropped his gaze. "That is old superstition only," he muttered. "It does not matter."

Dr. Blythe, who had been studying the male whooper, now quickly turned to the Indian. "I'm interested in this about the guardian spirit," he said. "I'd be grateful if you'd explain."

The Indian looked at him steadily and answered. "My people, the Tsa-Tcu, have known the giant birds as our good spirits. We know that when they leave our valley, we leave."

He shrugged. "It is as well. We will go to the reservation. The white man has won again."

Dr. Blythe thought for a moment, then made a decision. "Just a minute. I feel strongly that these birds should be kept in captivity and I think I can convince my colleagues of this. I will convince them. And I will get support for my experiment. But keeping them in captivity doesn't mean keeping them in a city zoo. Oh no. I say, let's try it right in your valley."

"Hooray!" It was a cry of joy from Jeff.

Dr. Blythe was thinking fast. "Of course! And who better to look after them than Eagle Eye and his family? It will take a lot of organization, work, and money. But I'm a very persuasive man when it comes to whooping cranes."

Big smiles were spreading over the faces of the Indians.

"Yes, yes indeed," Dr. Blythe rushed on. "We can devise large portable pens for the birds that can be moved around the valley to food supplies. They will be remote from all humans, except the Tsa-Tcu, who have always lived here. Winter? Well, we can manage that too. By then we should have a proper diet worked out and the food can be flown in regularly. I think it might work. I think it might. At least, we can certainly try!"

"That's wonderful!" Meg Gardner exclaimed, smiling. "Just wonderful!"

Dr. Blythe put his arms round the shoulders of Jeff and Eagle Eye. "Together you may have saved the whooping cranes," he said.

Mattie couldn't resist giving a small cheer.

Later, after all arrangements had been made, Jeff and Eagle Eye stood on the shore together. Oscar sat on his master's shoulder and pecked at his ear. It was time to say goodbye, and Jeff was sad.

Ever since Eagle Eye's arrival, Jeff had been trying to express his feelings but couldn't find the words. Suddenly he took the binocular strap from around his neck and held the binoculars out to his friend. "I want you to take these," he said. "They will help you to watch the birds."

The Indian boy took the glasses and held them in his hand.

"Thank you, Jeff," he said. "It is a great gift." He looked Jeff straight in the eye. "I see now that all white men do not just kill and destroy. I thank you for helping me learn that."

He got into the canoe with his father and uncle. Jeff watched him leave the shore. "I'll see you next summer," he shouted. Then he turned quickly away and walked back to the tent.

White Cloud

G. L. Carefoot

The boy squeezed to the ground and slithered toward the thin fringe of rushes that edged the lake. The young spring sun was already heavy with heat. But the boy didn't feel the hot sun, nor the rough stubble of last year's rushes, nor even the clouds of mosquitoes that swarmed above him as he crawled his way along. He inched himself over the last ten feet and slowly raised himself up on his elbows. His eyes widened. Across the narrow channel of water, he saw her. The great white bird was sitting on a nest of brown rushes, moss, and downy feathers, on the ruins of the old muskrat house.

Now she turned her head in a long, graceful curve, searching the rushes for the tiny sounds that had disturbed her. The boy was close enough to see the glint of fear in the brown eyes that stared out above the black beak. He waited until she turned her head again. The beak *was* black — no hint of yellow — the whole beak was black — jet black.

He sucked in a lungful of air, as though to draw into him the whole picture of the bird, and began inching backward. It seemed like an hour before he dared to raise himself to look. There, far away, beyond the green patch of rushes, gleamed a white spot.

When the boy reached his home, his mother met him at the door of the log cabin, her hands on her hips.

"Where have you been? You're almost an hour late! Now get right back to those lessons!"

"Mother, I know what kind they are! I got up close! There's no yellow on the beak. They *are* trumpeter swans!"

Now the boy spent every spare minute crouched behind the fringe of rushes at the far end of the lake. The pen swan never left the nest, except to rise and roll the eggs over with her bill. Her mate, the cob, cruised nearby with a watchful eye on the shore.

One day the pen swan seemed restless. She kept raising herself, arching her long neck as if to look at the eggs, and then settling down again. The time of hatching had come. From his blind of rushes the boy could almost hear the sharp tapping of the cygnets as they tried to pip the eggshells. He crouched lower, so intent that there seemed nothing else in the whole world but himself and the great white swan with her breast against the pipping eggs.

At last the mother bird stepped from the nest, nuzzled with her long, black beak, and settled down again, her outspread wings covering five quivering cygnets.

The boy let out his breath and backed away through his path in the rushes. From the far end of the lake came the clear, brassy notes of the male swan.

It was three days before the boy went back to the lake. As he peered through the fringe of rushes, he gasped, a groan came from his lips.

The nest was empty!

He was on his feet in a second, and then quickly he dropped down again.

There they were! Just like a flotilla of ships — the cob in front, the pen behind, and the five cygnets stretched out in single file between them.

His eyes glistened as he watched the little ones.

One cygnet was as white as the shining glacier that hung on the great mountain far away beyond the lake. The other four were as gray as sticks in the old muskrat house. The family of swans circled slowly around the bay. Then the cob and the pen stretched their long necks down to the muddy bottom, and five balls of fluff darted about the glassy surface.

The boy went to the lake every day the next week. The parents kept a close watch on the little ones, scanning the shoreline for signs of danger, for the shoreline was where danger lurked.

One day when the father and mother birds were stretching down their necks and feasting on the juicy water plants, the five small cygnets, with the white one leading, wandered off and paddled along the edge of the rushes. They came so close the boy could see their little eyes sharp with curiosity. Then they wheeled like a line of ships and passed around the point.

Suddenly there was a commotion, and the five little cygnets, shrieking and fluttering their stubby wings, came hurrying back in terror. Right behind them streaked a dark form.

The boy jumped to his feet, yelling and waving his arms. A swish of wings cut the air in front of him and a mass of white hit the dark form. There was a flurry of white wings and splashing water, and then a terrified loon, its outstretched wings flapping the water, streaked frantically down the lake with the cob swan hot behind.

The boy shuddered and began his backward crawl along the path. When he looked back, the two swans were herding the little ones along — well away from the shore.

It was a whole month before the boy saw the swans again. He had had to go timber cruising with his father away up north of the road to Bella Coola.

The very first thing he did when he got back was to take the trail to the far end of the lake. His eyes rounded in disbelief when he peered through the rushes. The cygnets, cruising along near the shore, seemed twice as big as when he had last seen them.

Then the great idea came to him!

The next day he came with dry crusts in his pocket. When he tossed the crumbs over the rushes, the cygnets started paddling out into the lake. But the boy waited. The cygnets glided to a stop and veered around. The crumbs were floating only a few yards from shore. The white cygnet, now the biggest by far, began paddling back, with the others following.

In a few days the white one was stretching his neck among the rushes to snatch the bread from the boy's hand. And the old swans, cruising farther out in the lake, just looked on. The boy meant no harm — they knew — they had always known.

The old swans knew danger.

One day when the boy was throwing out his last handful of crumbs, a call came from the mother swan — a low note, uttered twice — not loud, but of a timbre that set the young ones paddling. The boy twisted quietly around. There, among the bushes up on the ridge behind and scarcely visible, was a coyote, his yellow eyes squinting in the bright sunlight.

"You needn't worry about the coyote getting at your young swans," said the boy's father that evening. "Those swans can look after themselves. In fact, it would be better for them if you weren't around there at all."

It was early August. The boy skipped along the path to the lake, and now his pockets were filled with grain from the chicken house. The blind of rushes was all trampled down, for the young swans always seemed to know when he was coming and they would scramble up the bank to greet him.

He had emptied his pockets one evening and was sitting on the flattened clump of rushes watching the cygnets chase after water bugs. The white cygnet was swimming just beyond the tall grass. Something made the boy lift his eyes. In the tall grass behind the muskrat house at the other side of the little bay shone two yellow eyes.

As the coyote sprang, the cygnet ducked sideways and the snapping jaws missed their mark just by a feather.

The boy jumped up — but the old swan was faster. Zooming in, he swooped on the coyote before he could turn and, rising in the water, struck again and again with the knuckles of his great white wings. It was all over in a minute. The bedraggled coyote, yelping and dragging one leg, slithered up the bank and disappeared into the bushes.

His father was right — those swans certainly could look after themselves.

It was a gray day in late August. Now the young ones were fully feathered and almost as tall as the boy. The white one had lately taken to helping himself from the boy's jacket pocket as the others gobbled up the grain from the ground. And after they had cleaned up the last kernel of wheat, the white one always stayed for the boy to stroke his neck.

But this day scudding clouds were piling over the high mountains in the west, and the wind was starting to come up the lake in heavy gusts. The boy quickly emptied all his pockets and, head down, hurried back up the path. When he reached the ridge top, he almost collided with the old man in the battered brown hat. He was wrinkled, and weathered as brown as the bark of the tree trunk he was standing under. And he was looking down toward the lake where the swans were feeding in the shallows behind the old muskrat house.

It was Charlie Joe, and under his arm he was carrying a parcel wrapped up in a newspaper.

"They are big," said Charlie Joe. "Soon they will fly."

"Yes," the boy answered.

"You feed the young ones."

"Yes. . . . My father says that no one can shoot trumpeter swans. They are protected by law."

The old man seemed not to hear. He was staring at the swans. Abruptly he turned and handed the parcel to the boy.

"Here is some young venison. It's good and tender. I have to hurry; there's a storm coming."

Charlie Joe pointed to the west and disappeared behind the tall spruce trees on the ridge.

It was early October and frosts had turned the birches up on the high ground to a pale yellow. The nights were sharp with cold, and in the mornings a thin film of ice glazed the still water among the rushes at the edge of the lake.

Now the cygnets were fully grown young swans, and they flew endlessly — strengthening their wings for the long journey into the cold, thin air and over the high mountains to the west in search of an ice-free lake and a winter home.

Every evening as the boy walked down the path with his big tin can full of wheat, he watched them cutting across the red sunset of the sky. Their triumphant buglings echoed up and down the lake. As he approached his old blind in the rushes, the young swans wheeled in, landing with whistling splashes and paddling ashore. The white one had grown into a magnificent cob, almost as big as the father bird.

It was late October now, and one evening Charlie Joe came, on his way to the reservation up Bella Coola way. He talked about swans. His grandfather had told him that many years before the white man came, the lake had been white with swans. The swans had brought the Indians good luck — "many big fat deer and moose". But now none came back.

"White men are bad for swans," said Charlie.

And his grandfather had told him that when a swan died, it didn't die — it changed into a white cloud — not an ordinary white cloud, but a fluffy white cloud that floated and floated away across the sky.

The boy stayed awake a long time that night, thinking and

worrying. His white swan did look like a fluffy white cloud when he ruffled up his feathers and sailed along so quietly it scarcely made a ripple on the still lake.

It was the first week in November. A few big, wet snowflakes were floating down from a leaden sky, as the boy dragged himself slowly back from the lake — with his tin can still full of grain. The swans had gone, the lake was empty.

It was December, cold and white. The boy's mother had just knocked the hot, crisp loaves out of their tins when Charlie Joe knocked at the door. He handed her a parcel wrapped up in an old Vancouver newspaper.

"Fresh moose — young fat cow!"

Without another word Charlie turned and walked away.

As the boy's mother unwrapped the meat, her eye caught the heading in large type: RARE TRUMPETER SWANS SHOT NEAR CAMPBELL RIVER

She carefully walked with the paper to the boy's room.

It was the Saturday before Christmas. The boy and his father had plodded up through a foot of light, dry snow to the benchland behind the birches for a Christmas tree. His father pointed to a bushy spruce. "Isn't this one a dandy, son?"

But the boy was not looking at the tree. In the late afternoon sun, the snowy lake sparkled like millions of diamonds — and over the bay of the muskrat house the boy saw a fluffy white cloud that floated away across the sky.

Trumpets Over the Northland

John Patrick Gillese

The night before the lake froze, the trumpeter swans flew excitedly around the Grande Prairie countryside, honking farewell to the land of the mighty Peace. It is always their prelude to departing for their wintering grounds in the South.

But three — hatched late on a lake near Clairmont, Alberta — could not manage even the initial take-off. The Tomshacks, homesteaders in the Peace River country, found them stranded on the frozen farmlands, and began a unique experiment in domesticating the trumpeters. That was in 1945, four years before the Canadian Wildlife Service made Bernard Hamm Migratory Bird Officer for the area, and special guardian to the world's rarest swans.

The Tomshacks' trio soon became family pets. Though they thought nothing of routing a calf or dog, they'd rest their regal heads in human hands, hunt for tidbits with their big black beaks, "tweeter" deep thanks in their throats. Every Winter afternoon the trumpeters would fly for a couple of hours about the famous wheat country — keeping their wings strong, working off the nervousness that is part of their nature.

In time they adopted humans so completely that when the Tomshacks went visiting, or took off for Grande Prairie for groceries, the swans would follow, flying some 50 feet above the car. While the family shopped, they circled over the town, trumpeting anxiously until the car started homeward again. Clearly, they knew not only the Tomshacks' automobile, but the honk of its horn; and it was a touching drama to see them sailing gracefully above a line of traffic on the highway, ignoring the coaxing horns of other motorists, but trumpeting a great bass bugle-blare of love when the Tomshacks honked at them.

"Intelligent?" asks Bernard Hamm. "Judge for yourself."

The Spring of 1947, marked by an early thaw, proved

something of the depth of swan devotion as well. That year, two of the Tomshacks' tame swans betook themselves to the slush of Mercer Hill, near Clairmont. One was killed by a passing car.

"I mounted the dead swan" — Bernard Hamm was telling me the story while we drove from Sexsmith to Wolf Lake, 45 miles northwest of Grande Prairie — "but ever after the survivor would savagely attack any car that came near the Tomshack yard. Those great wings of his could dent the hood!"

Perhaps "Tommy" — the survivor — also remembered that the driver had been a man. More and more he gave his devotion to womenfolk.

"All they had to do was go out in the yard with a loaf of bread," Barney Hamm recalled. "Tommy would wag his wings and come running. But he never forgave men for the loss of his mate. Once he actually broke up a ball game in Clairmont!"

We got out of the car. Clouds of Lapland longspurs rose from the fields around us. It was early May — time of the great return to the tundras.

The 60-year-old naturalist, who has been studying Canadian wildlife for fully 45 years, adjusted the camera tripod and invited me to look over Wolf Lake. Through the powerful sighting scope I got my first breath-taking look at white royalty. Seemingly only a few feet away, two cloud-white trumpeters were feeding casually against the far shore, long powerful necks nipping the Richardson's pondweed from the lake bottom. There was something unforgettably majestic in the way they turned suddenly — wary, even at that distance.

"They've decided to stay." From years of studying them, Hamm can interpret their every movement. "Now this is their lake."

On the sun-polished waters, eared grebes chuckled, pintails peep-peeped, coots gabbled incessantly. The swans are tolerant of such lesser fowl, but they permit no rival royalty — none of the lordly Canada geese, for example. Their hatred of geese amounts almost to mania.

Barney told me of a fearful fight between a Canada gander and a trumpeter swan on Flying Shot Lake, southwest of Grande Prairie. The intruding goose was whipped, its wing bone broken close to the socket. It crawled two miles from the lake before death overtook it. Hamm shipped it to Indiana University.

Equally fearsome was the fate of a big, good-natured domestic goose kept in a barnyard on the edge of Hermit Lake. The male swan, flying around the lake one day, spotted the goose on the ground, attacked it almost on the farmer's doorstep, and beat it to a bloody pulp.

The swans are kings! Not even other swans are allowed within half a mile of a nesting site — and so, generally, each of the numerous small lakes around Grande Prairie supports a single pair of trumpeter swans.

"There is no living creature around — not even a man in a canoe — that could tangle with them in water and live," Barney believes.

Their weight alone is a factor; the average male weighs about 26 pounds, the female 23. Yet they recognize the kindly man who paddles among them Summer after Summer. They see him sitting in a canoe a foot or two from their nests, but the brown eyes shine only with affection, and no great wings roar up for battle shock. The young actually wait for him to band and handle them!

The royal couple on Wolf Lake were house hunting in the cattails. Their nest, built preferably atop an abandoned muskrat bailiwick, is a crude place of slough grasses and mud, on which the pen lays an egg every other day, till the usual setting of five or six is complete. (The most Hamm ever found in a nest was nine.) The eggs are huge — about five inches long by three inches in diameter — tapering off at both ends, the color of washed-out lime. After 36 to 38 days, fluffy-white cygnets, bigger than week-old turkey poults, take a royal tumble into the world of sky-blue waters.

These small, shallow lakes, scattered over 1,500 square miles of Grande Prairie countryside, represent the last hope of saving the magnificent bird whose numbers once sailed almost every slough on the Canadian prairies. There are trumpeters at Lonesome Lake, British Columbia, though no one has found the nesting sites; also at Red Rock Refuge in the United States. There may be a few in the Mackenzie District of the Northwest Territories, near the tundra. But wildlife experts consider Grande Prairie as the last replenishing ground; and it was largely at the urging of conservation experts in both countries — men like Arthur S. Hawkins, of the Illinois State Natural History Division, and J. Dewey Soper, of the Canadian Wildlife Service — that the Canadian Government appointed Hamm to his extraordinary job. In recognition they have since bestowed on him the singular title "Guardian of the Trumpeter Swans".

For Barney — farmer, trapper, guide, and outdoorsman — it's the finest work in the world. Born in Gretna, Manitoba (on the U.S. border), in 1900, he skipped school to study wildlife. By 16 he was teaching himself taxidermy — and later, Dr. William Rowan, an authority on bird migration, told me that Hamm's work ranked with the best he had ever seen. It was inevitable, almost, that he should become a key man with Ducks Unlimited. The moment he set eyes on the South Peace he recognized it as a mecca for birdbanding. There, under the shelter of the nearby Rockies, age-old flyways converge; there, weary migrants settle down for rest and food before flying on to the Arctic. In the past decade Hamm has banded at least 10,000 international travellers.

But for seven months of every year, Bernard Hamm's main job is to see that the remnants of the royal trumpeters rest and raise their progeny in peace. By car and canoe, in storm and sun, he patrols the lowland of lakes and farmlands, preaches conservation in as many as ten schoolrooms a week ("the kids of today are the conservationists of tomorrow"), sets up wildlife exhibits at the county fair, and pays tribute to the people around him "for the kind of cooperation that has saved the trumpeter from extinction".

Disaster seeks out the great birds in many expected forms — from a bald eagle fixing his shaggy glare on a cygnet far below, to men big enough to carry guns but not big enough to leave a rare and lovely bird, with a ten-foot wingspread, alone. But it comes in unexpected ways as well.

Muskrats, for example, may undermine the nesting structures. In one such, four eggs dropped through; and, as Barney puts it, "the birds gave up in despair and deserted the whole thing."

The Spring of 1956 was particularly bad in this respect. The previous Autumn, muskrats were so plentiful that Hamm counted more then 100 houses on one small lake. That Winter the overcrowded 'rats starved, literally eating one another out of house and home. When the nesting trumpeters took over in Spring, the structures collapsed under their weight.

During the long nesting the birds never relax vigilance, and both become tremendously excited when the moment of hatching arrives. Thus, on a nest with nine eggs, one pair of proud parents swam off, trumpeting the joyful news, when the first three cygnets hatched. In their excitement they completely forgot the six unhatched eggs!

If the parents become ill, they abandon their young without hesitation. Some wildlife men will tell you that the swans are intelligent enough to realize that a sick adult might infect a healthy cygnet. In the Fall, if the young can't fly, they are left to their fate — but, again, reason wins out over the birds' deep family sense. Once the lakes freeze — almost invariably about the 23rd-25th of October — the swans *must* go south or perish.

Low-flying planes frighten the trumpeters. Sometimes Barney finds a swan killed by power lines or telephone wires. Lake leeches — black bloodsuckers — will attach themselves to the swans' nostrils and slowly sup their life away. Hamm spends long hours hunting around the lakes for cygnets that simply "disappear" — and it is largely due to his efforts that the swans today number about 1,500, compared to an appalling 80 or 90 during the drought-ridden '30s. Even so, the loss of a single cygnet is tragic.

Some clue to the trumpeter's insistence on undisputed privacy comes in the Fall, when the young learn to fly. If Canada geese need runways, so do the huge swans: they splatter the watertop for almost 100 yards before getting airborne! But once aloft, long legs and black feet tucked in their snow-white feathers, there is no more thrilling picture. Their wild bugle notes carry for two miles across the Autumn sky.

For excitement, this period surpasses all others. Bugled at and berated by the parents — who know full well the significance of shrinking shorelines and coloring softwoods — the cygnets will stand by the hour on muskrat houses, flapping and exercising their wings. If all else fails to make the timid ones take to the air, the adults thresh them within an inch of their lives. Small wonder the cygnets welcome the sight of their human guardian and his canoe! Like all well-bred people, the swans lay off domestic disputes when company comes.

But the old cobs know the necessity of such stern training. When the lake freezes over, it is too late to learn to fly. Those who fail must stay behind.

That is when Bernard Hamm makes his last patrols, collecting the beautiful, bewildered stragglers and shipping them to such refuges as the Delta in Manitoba. Silence settles over the lakes of the South Peace — silence unbroken until the excited blare of trumpets, sounding above the April storm, declares that the swans are home again.

The Plowing

Delbert A. Young

There was an air of general alarm. From her nest in the grey stubble, a little spoonbill duck felt it, recognized it as a danger to the eight eggs beneath her.

So far the cause of it was down at the other end of the field. Crows were rising, wheeling about, settling again with harsh cries. There were horses. But horses were not dangerous, unless a huge foot came directly down on the nest.

These horses though, were not acting in a normal manner. They were not wandering about cropping the grass. They were marching, several of them abreast. The duck could hear a man's voice. As the horses drew nearer, she could see that something was following behind. On the thing sat a man, a floppy hat on his head to protect his eyes from the June sun.

The duck was worried. This had seemed such a safe place to build a nest. The tall, last year stubble blended so well with her brown feathers. Once, it had fooled a coyote. The gaunt creature had stopped to sniff at mice runs only yards away. She had sat so still, so like a clump of dirt, the coyote hadn't seen her.

But this was more frightening than the coyote. She shifted a trifle on her nest, gazed down the field with her sharp little eyes.

As the outfit — that's what it was — passed fifty yards to the west of the spoonbill, a black ribbon stretched out behind it. The duck stirred uneasily. She had a dim memory of another year, a year when she hadn't taken any ducklings down to the water. There had been horses that other time. Horses, and a man, and crows wheeling noisily about.

Instinctively, she knew. The farmer was plowing his field and the crows were following behind, picking up insects — or eggs.

A pair of frightened Hungarian partridges flew low and swiftly past the spoonbill. Their nest was already in danger. The trampling of the horses, the general excitement, had startled the hen off her eggs. When the horses had reached the far end of the field and the uproar had died down, the two Huns returned.

The hubbub continued all afternoon. Then there was silence. The farmer had unhitched and gone home, the crows had departed.

The spoonbill waited until deep dusk. Then she got off her nest and flew straight away. She wasn't leaving any tracks for a skunk, or a weasel, to find and follow. It was only a two-hundred-yard flight to the rush-rimmed slough.

She stayed there long enough to allow the eggs to cool a trifle. When she rose from the water, she did it carefully. She was trying to keep some of the moisture on her feathers. The shells of the eggs needed that moisture to keep them from being so hard that a duckling could not chip them. When she arrived at the nest, she turned each egg over with her odd-shaped bill. That done, she settled for the night.

Next day, the farmer and his horses were closer — much closer. New land had been broken out and the duck could hear the man more clearly now, as he talked. She could hear the plow rattling and squeaking. The din of the crows was louder also. At times, there would be crows only yards away. The duck remained motionless. Just before noon, the two Hungarians trailed away from their smashed nest. They walked through the tall stubble, passing within feet of the duck, making small, plaintive sounds of mourning to each other. Later they returned, to perch on the blackened earth above where their nest had been.

By mid-afternoon, the duck could feel the earth tremble slightly from the solid tread of the draft horses each time they passed. She felt panic. But she refused to desert her eggs.

Suddenly, a crow landed a yard away. For a few seconds he and the duck gazed at each other.

"Caw! Caw! Caw!" the crow was opening its mouth and closing it, and bobbing its head in eagerness. A dozen others came quickly. They fluttered down, filled the air with their harsh scolding.

This was an old game which the black robbers enjoyed. They were confident this little brown duck would be as stupid as the Hungarian partridge had been. The crows found their nest. They had watched it, annoying the hen until the outfit came close. The bird had panicked, slipped off the nest. Immediately, the crows had pounced down, driving their ugly beaks into the eggs.

The plow on its next trip around had covered what was left, some bits of shell and mussed grass and down. But no bird, certainly no other duck, has the courage of the spoonbill. This one continued to sit, refusing to stir an inch, even when the feet of the outside horse came within four feet of her.

Next time around, she would be under the big horse's feet.

They were coming now. The duck could feel the earth vibrate. The farmer was talking to the animals. The mountainous beasts towered straight ahead. The crows rose up, flew screaming away.

Suddenly the man shouted. The outfit stopped. The duck was looking upward into the face of the nearest horse. The animal bowed his head, sneezed loudly to clear the dust from his nostrils. The duck remained as still as if she were a brown decoy and not a living bird at all.

Again she heard footsteps. These footsteps were light. The farmer was coming up in front of his horses. He stopped, stood looking down at the duck for a long time. A couple of crows returned and lit close by. The man shook his fist at them. He gazed down upon the spoonbill again, appeared to be trying to decide something. Finally, he began to talk.

To the duck, his voice was not unpleasant. She found it strangely soft and reassuring. Then it was silent again. The man turned, walked back to his plow. He spoke to the horses. The earth shook once more.

It shook. The big horses came one step closer. Then they veered sharply to the left. Big feet stomped by, a foot away from the tiny duck.

When they had passed and the jingle of trace chains was growing faint, an oblong of grey stubble surrounded the nest. On all sides of it was moist, black earth.

The crows came back. They cawed louder than ever. The odd one flew up and made short dives at the duck, coming within inches of her before they levelled out. The boldest came almost close enough to peck at her. He opened his ugly beak and screamed and screamed.

The duck sat unblinking, unmoved. Cowards, she knew them to be.

Finally, the farmer quit for the night. The sun went down. The crows left and all was quiet.

It was dark now. The spoonbill hadn't made her trip down to the slough for food and water. The faint but bitter scent of a skunk hung in the air. The little duck was parched, her body crying for moisture after its long vigil. But she dare not leave the eggs now. Her instincts told her that this was the night the miracle would occur. A couple of times she thrust her misshapen bill underneath her body, nuzzled the eggs. Satisfied, she resumed her position.

Soon there was a tiny movement below her breast. More and more the movement increased, spread, until the nest was alive. The spoonbill sat perfectly still.

One hour, two hours passed. Then the duck got up and turned around. She felt with her bill each of the seven tiny ducklings which huddled together seeking warmth from their first blast of cold air. She rooted out the lone egg that was left. It was sterile. That done, she sat back down, spreading her wings a trifle to afford more cover for the ducklings.

She remained that way until a flush showed in the east. A faint light began to steal across the blackened field. She had to move fast. It was 200 yards down to the slough. The crows would come with the sun.

When John Millar made his first trip down the field that morning, he stopped his horses opposite the oblong of stubble. He walked the few steps over and stood gazing down at the empty nest. It was all mussed now and the crows had eaten the sterile egg.

He put a work-hardened hand up to this head, scratched it thoughtfully. When he looked down toward the slough, he smiled. His keen old eyes could see a mother duck and her brood out in the middle of it.

He was a good farmer, was John Millar. He spoke aloud. "I'm tickled you fooled the black devils," he said. "And now I can swing around and finish plowing my field."

goshawk
Gary Geddes

disdainful
            lording it
over the common ground

prince of air currents
the goshawk circles
            each muscle
a slave to his reconnaissance

behind unblinking eyes
a small brain studies precise
aerial photographs
singlemindedly

                    he drops
himself his own bombardment
seizes the moment with claws
that will rip and shred

my rifle brings him down
the victim's victim dead
but intact
            a single feather
hangs in the sky

and clouds

The Decision

Gordon Pellerin

Snap!

I jumped to my feet. I had been lying on the bank for about two hours waiting to hear the clang of that rusty old beaver trap. I tripped over a small stump and slid through a patch of lilics in my haste to reach the complex mound of sticks and mud where my "tunnel of death" had just played its role.

This miniature creek, inhabited by beavers, runs through my father's land. The beavers had removed a large number of trees which regulated the flow of the creek, and it had flooded, destroying a large portion of our yearly crops. Therefore, my dad had obtained a license giving us permission to trap the beavers. The trap my dad had purchased was a rusty square which, when placed on a beaver's slippery mud runway, snapped closed, crushing the victim as it tripped the wire.

I reached the edge of the cliff where, below, about 20 feet, the creek had formed a small pond due to a gigantic, partially completed beaver dam. I clambered down the steep drop of the bank, the musky perfume of the creek and the piney fragrance of the dark evergreens assaulting my nose in a desperate struggle for supremacy. Hurriedly, I reached the pile of symmetrically balanced sticks and twigs, glued together with mud, that was the dam. Sticks split and cracked beneath my feet as I pounded across. At the age of twelve, I had caught my first beaver.

Bright red blood oozed slowly from the big nostrils and stained the damp ground. I lifted, pulled open the mouth of the trap, and let the mound of flesh slip out dropping with a hollow thud to the concrete-like surface of the dam.

As soon as I had reset the trap, I grabbed the rough, wet tail and began dragging the beaver up the precipitous creek bank. Blood gushed from its mouth and nostrils and oozed down the abrupt slope to be absorbed into the crumbling soil. On the level surface again, in the middle of a small clearing, I dug a shallow pit into which I dropped the carcass. The old hog landed on his belly in the pit, his soft fur reflecting the sunlight that penetrated the grave. Shortly, however, the shiny fur was concealed beneath gooey, cold black soil as I entombed the stiffening body.

Finished, I strolled along the twisting creek homeward. Gradually, I began to wonder. How could such an industrious, non-aggressive little animal cause so much damage? He wasn't malicious; it was just natural for a beaver to perform such acts. Didn't beavers have a right to live, too? What right had I to destroy them?

I thought about it all the way home. Instead of trekking across the muddy summer-fallowed field, I strolled all the way around by the creek to the main crossing. A cool breeze carried the scent of the fresh spring afternoon after a rain. My feet crushed white lilies and bright, butter-yellow buttercups which formed a damp carpet over the entire uncultivated stretch of land. The tall green deciduous trees towered over the creek, seeming to fall as the clouds sped by overhead.

As I slid down the steady slope of the crossing, I could hear the burbling creek flowing over the large rocks which formed the trail. The water was bright and clear with the hot sun's reflected rays on its surface. At the edge, I removed my muddy shoes and socks and waded into the cold runoff from the snows higher up. All was silent except for the murmur of the creek as it fell over large rocks and the faint "putt" of an old diesel tractor pulling an ancient Cockshutt seeder off across the fields. I climbed the opposite bank to the freshly seeded barley field.

I spent the next few weeks working in the fields. However, I did get time to maintain the small trap. I caught a beaver nearly every day, and every day, standing on the unfinished dam looking at my quarry, I was more and more disturbed by the unnaturalness of what I was doing. I thought to myself, "Do I really want to destroy these creatures? They don't deserve this." I thought about my duty to rid the farm of them. I thought, "The world is divided into two groups, the hunters and the hunted. It is my duty, as a hunter, to prevent our crops from being flooded. Therefore, I must kill the beavers . . . the hunted."

My dilemma began to haunt me. What was right? Kill them! No, free them! Let them live naturally in this naturally beautiful creek.

Kill them! They are destroying your year's work. Kill them! Free them . . . !

Finally, one hot, dry afternoon, I arrived at the dam to find a young beaver pup, alive in the trap. I inspected the trap and discovered a twig had lodged itself between the two killing ends preventing their crushing force from reaching the pup. He couldn't escape but he wasn't hurt. His bushy fur was golden fluffy and I couldn't help petting him. There was no telling how long he had been held captive in the heat.

The air was desperately hot and dry and the voices spoke again, "Kill! Free! Kill! Free!"

I faltered there for what seemed like hours. Finally, I leaned over, unhooked the mouth of the trap and allowed the pup to slide slowly out unharmed. On his fat belly, he slid down the greasy runway and wriggled into the water. "What are my parents going to say?" I wondered.

"I want that beaver dead! Now!" ordered my father after I told him. Desperate, I returned to the dam to reset the trap. I placed a round tree branch, which had been stripped of its bark by the beavers, between the two killing ends so they could not catch the pup. I might be able to convince my father that the beaver had left. Still, I worried that the stick might not hold the trap open.

I waited a couple of days before going back to the twist in the creek. But when I did, I wished I hadn't. Under the bending branches of the willow bushes lay the trap and the beaver pup was in it, dead this time.

I scrambled down and squatted beside the trap, petting the soft misshapen body. Gradually, I grew aware of a silence in the creek valley. I no longer heard the running water of the creek as it penetrated the unfinished dam. Checking, I discovered that earlier, the beaver pup had pulled the stick out of the trap and used it as the final piece to complete the unbelievably large and concrete structure. Already, the water was backing up, forming a small lake, and rising to lap at my feet.

Of course, we bombed the dam, completely destroying it. The pond is gone too, and the cattle have cropped off most of the flowers. Only a thin trickle runs down the gully now, and dead trees and pointed grey stumps line its banks. I don't go there any more.

Skipper for Keeps

D. P. Barnhouse

A passing truck dropped Skipper at their gate one drizzly July evening. Toby, busy picking cockle burrs out of Midge's tail, watched the old man standing uncertainly beside his big canvas sack. Midge growled and her hackles rose up.

"Friend of yours?" Toby asked Billy Ekhart, the hired man. Billy wiped his harmonica on his sleeve and peered through the drizzle at the white-capped, pea-jacketed stranger.

"No friend of mine," Billy said. "Looks like a seafarin' bloke." Toby clattered down the veranda steps.

When he got closer, he saw that their visitor was even older than he'd seemed at a distance. A snowy thatch and beard frosted the lined, leather-brown face. The blue eyes were squinty, as though from too much looking into the sun. Toby noticed the words stamped on the canvas sea bag . . . *Nancy B, Newfoundland*. Where had he seen them before? Then he remembered. The same words, in tiny gold letters, were on the black hull of the painted schooner that hung over their mantel.

"I'm Toby Ryner." He held out his hand and was surprised at the strength in the gnarled one that gripped it.

"Couldn't be nobody else." The sea-blue eyes twinkled. "I'm Skipper and I've come to stop a spell."

It was as simple as that . . . almost as though a giant wave, sweeping inland from the far and mighty Atlantic, had deposited him here in the middle of their prairie farmyard — to "stop a spell".

"Why do you suppose he picked us?" Toby asked his mother one evening after the old man had gone to bed.

"Because we're kinfolk, I expect, and maybe because your father went to sea with him once, when he wasn't much older than you." She sighed. "I wish I knew what to do with him."

"Why can't he just stay on here with us?"

"You're pretty fond of him, aren't you?"

"It's nice having someone to talk to — about 'different' things," he said quickly, not wanting to hurt her feelings.

"It's just that I'm afraid of losing Billy," his mother said with a worried frown. "He's getting real edgy; says it's like having two cooks in a kitchen. I couldn't run this place without Billy."

They'd had a succession of hired men since his father died, but none worth his salt till Billy came. He was a dandy worker, but in the conversation department, well, compared to Billy a clam was a big blabber mouth. The only one he ever talked to was his sheepdog, Midge — except when he got steamed up, like he did when Skipper cut a hole in the feed shed.

"That chuckleheaded old bluenose has gone and cut a hole in the roof," he stormed, "just so he can shoot the stars with a sextet."

"*Sextant,*" Toby said. "That's for charting a course."

"Yeah," Billy growled, "straight to the booby hatch. I tell you, Miz Ryner, the old geezer makes me nervous as an aspen in a high wind. . . . Can't tell what in Sam Hill he'll do next!"

"Now, Billy," his mother soothed. "He's just a confused old man, and he misses the sea."

"Misses it, my foot! He just packed it up in that old sea bag and dumped it here in the middle of Alberta. With all that seagoing gear in the shed there's hardly room for a feed sack. I tell you I won't have him messing around, getting in my way." Billy Ekhart just had no imagination, Toby decided.

But his mother had always said that honey caught more flies than vinegar. . . . "I'll keep a sharp eye on Skipper, Mom, and I could help Billy more with the chores . . ."

"Maybe he would be better off in a home with other old people," his mother mused.

"He won't bother Billy any more, you'll see."

"Well . . . ," his mother said, "we'll wait a bit and see what happens."

132   WildLife?

Nothing did happen for a while, except for the fire, and that didn't amount to much.

"It's just that Skipper dozes off sometimes," Toby explained, "and he forgets about his pipe."

Billy didn't say anything but he wore that "I told you so" look, and he made a great to-do about replacing the burned floor boards.

Then there was the business of the traps and Ron Jenkins' father declaring that Skipper was a public nuisance. Ron was a great one for setting traps and Skipper was a great one for unsetting them. He had once shipped on a sealer to Labrador; he had no stomach for wasteful slaughter.

"Soon there'll be no seals left on the Eastern seaboard," he said, "and if some folks have their way, there'll be no wild creatures left on these prairies either."

Surprisingly, Billy Ekhart took this latest crisis and Mr. Jenkins' complaints quite calmly.

"Skins aren't worth a hang this time of year anyhow," Billy said shortly. "I'll swear that kid puts out traps for pure meanness."

But the frown furrows reappeared on his mother's face, and Toby's misery tightened like a coiled snake.

"It's right what Billy says, Mom. Ron Jenkins don't need those skins."

"Doesn't!" she corrected. "If there's one thing I don't want, it's trouble with the neighbors." Then she gave both Toby and Skipper a lecture on the dangers of interfering with private property.

That's when Toby started getting up earlier to rush through the chores so he could take Skipper on long walks. Once they caught some grayling in the creek, and Skipper showed his mother how to make them into a delicious fish chowder.

"Too bad you don't have any sea biscuit," he said mournfully. "Fish without brewis is like clouds without rain — plumb dishonest."

Another time they followed the creek to a beaver dam that edged some property owned by Mr. Jenkins. They found a beaver in a trap. Its leg was badly mangled and it had been dead for a long time. Skipper nosed around and found four more traps. He sprang each of them, then hurled them well out into the deep water above the dam. Even if Toby had felt like speaking, the Skipper's face would have discouraged him. They stood together, silently watching the circles spread out over the quiet face of the pool. It took quite a while for the last ripples to die away. They stayed there a little longer, not talking but hearing the fussing of blackbirds in the rushes and the whimpering cry of a loon a long way off.

On the way home they discovered the abandoned hay rack.

It stood near a windrow where Billy had done a second cutting of green feed. As they approached obliquely through the rib-high grain, its decks seemed awash in a golden flood tide.

"There's a foundered hulk," Skipper said. His gaze raked the horizon as though searching for something.

"I've never seen a real sailing ship," Toby said regretfully.

"You'd need to look a good piece nowadays, mate. Square-riggers, sloops, schooners . . . I've seen 'em so thick in the harbor you could walk their decks to Pimm's Light without dampening a shoe. There's a few of the old hulls still working the Grand Banks, but stripped down, with rumblers in their puddocks." He sighed deeply. "It's tall masts and canvas, son, that gives a ship dignity."

"You promised to tell me about the *Nancy B*," Toby reminded him.

"You hear tell of Cape Race?" Skipper asked. Toby nodded. "Well, many's the vessel's run afoul of those reefs and that's where the *Nance* lies — along of her own kind."

"But you had other ships after that?"

"Lashins of 'em, mate, but gowdy tubs they were, to be sure . . . no dignity, no character. Draggers and seiners I had aplenty, but no proper vessel after the *Nancy B*." The sea-blue eyes narrowed as he lifted the wagon tongue. "A long bowsprit she had, canted upward, like so; and a keel as deep as Willy's well; foremast about there . . . mainmast a little aft of centre."

"Billy just cut some new fence rails. They'd make dandy masts."

"We could lash up the bowsprit."

"There's binder twine and baling wire in the tool shed."

"She'd need sails."

"If we made up our beds first thing every day, maybe the sheets wouldn't be missed."

"By George!" Skipper said. "We'll make us a *real* prairie schooner."

In the days that followed it was as though the real *Nancy B* had risen from under her weight of fathoms to reveal to Toby the world of the sea that the Skipper had known — and Toby's father too, long before he was born.

Toby learned to rig a sea anchor, box the thirty-two points on the compass, take a sounding. Skipper's step had a new spring to it. Even Billy Ekhart left to himself, became good-humored — at least as good-humored as Billy could get.

A sort of golden sleep lay over the prairie as the fields waited for the harvesters. The misery in Toby's chest was so quiet he thought it had gone for good. Then suddenly it was back again.

He was whitewashing the stable when his mother came in, the frown furrows etched deeper than ever.

"Where's Skipper?" she asked.

"I don't know," Toby said. . . . "What do you want him for?"

"Mr. Jenkins was just here. He threatens to lay a charge. Did either of you two steal some of Ron's traps?"

"Of course we didn't *steal* them," he said hotly.

"Then tell me what you *did* do."

"You know how Skipper feels about . . . well . . . he sort of threw them in the creek."

"In that case," she said crossly, "we're in for trouble. Now you go and round up that old sinner before he gets into more mischief, while I figure out what to do."

Billy Ekhart sat on the end of the water trough, mending harness. Old Midge rested her head on his heavy boots like they were feather pillows.

"You see Skipper?" Toby asked.

"Not if I could help it," Billy said.

Toby checked the well house and the side porch, where the old man liked to doze in the hammock. He glanced down the long white road that stitched itself through a patchwork of fields and lost itself in blue distance. There was only one other place to look for Skipper.

Midge raised her head from Billy's boots and wuffled a greeting as Toby passed the water trough.

"Would she like to go for a run?" he asked Billy.

"Just ask her," Billy said slyly and winked at Midge. Toby whistled and the dog bounded joyfully forward. After a bit she looked back to see if Billy was coming. She whined coaxingly. When Billy didn't respond, she went back and lay down at his feet.

"Guess she just ain't in the mood," Billy said.

"That hound sure is getting old," said Toby testily. "No git up and go to her."

"Has when she's a mind to. Got more sense too than some folks I could mention."

Toby turned and walked away. He crossed the north pasture, then followed the swath left by the binder. The stubble prickled his feet, and field mice scurried for cover under the bundles of green feed. Beyond the clump of poplars that concealed her from the house and roadway, the *Nancy B*'s sails fluttered in the breeze like great cabbage moths. There was only a narrow strip of standing grain on her starboard side, and wading through it Toby scrunched down so the rustling waves closed over his head.

When he popped up under the gunwales, Skipper was grinning down at him.

"Nigh harpooned you for a whale," he said. "Come aboard and give me a hand with this." Skipper had fashioned a sea hammock from an old binder belt. Toby helped him sling it between the masts and the old man climbed into it.

"You take this watch," he said, "and I'll take forty winks."

I'll tell him about Mr. Jenkins after his nap, Toby decided. Soon the old man was snoring gently. A rising wind flung molten spume against their bows.

A sudden gust rattled the rigging and Skipper sat bolt upright. "Haul the jib and reef the mainsail. We're in for a blow!"

Toby wrestled with the wheel. "Rudder's dead, sir." Just then he heard a dog's barking and the jingling of harness. He turned to see Billy Ekhart approaching up the windrow with the team of grays. Reluctantly, Toby loosened his grip on make-believe. Not so the Skipper. He knew how to spit in reality's eye.

"Craft ahoy!" he bellowed.

Billy pulled up. "How's that?" he said in a dazed sort of way.

"Pass us a tow line and stand by," Skipper shouted.

"Stow that stuff!" Billy said crossly. "I've got to haul in a load of green feed. You jokers clear off that rack."

"Oh no you don't! If we take to the boats you'll claim salvage. We're not abandoning this ship."

Billy rolled his eyes and circled his right ear with his index finger. Then he began manoeuvring the team into position for hitching up.

"Secure the line, mate," Skipper said.

Toby was annoyed by Billy's insulting gesture. "What the heck!" he thought, and busied himself securing the whiffletrees to the *Nancy*'s bowsprit. "Tow away!" he said and looked Billy squarely in the eye.

Billy snapped the reins in an irritated way. "Hey Nellie! Hey Boots!" he snarled. "Giddap hyah!" The team leaned into the traces, and slowly the *Nancy B* moved through the yellow sea, flags waving and all sails set.

Their course brought them within a few yards of the highway at one point, just at the time when Mr. Jenkins' station wagon hove into view. The expression on his face and the way his eyebrows tangled up in his hairline sent Skipper and Toby into a laughing fit. Midge, who had a sense of humor, racketed along in their wake, breasting the waves like a porpoise after a Tom cod. Billy hauled up and began pitchforking sheaves onto the deck. This sobered them like a dash of cold water. In a few minutes the *Nancy B* was dismantled and the day disenchanted. Toby, folding up Skipper's hammock, remembered that he had yet to warn him about the fix they were in. Suddenly he wondered what they'd found funny enough to laugh about.

Billy drove home by way of the slough to see how the late hay was doing. Toby dangled his legs over the edge of the rack and watched Midge chase frogs in the ditches. Skipper began to sing a Newfoundland sea chanty.

> There was birch rine, tar twine, cherry wine,
> and turpentine
> Jowls and calabogus, ginger beer and tea,
> Pigs' feet, cat's meat, dumplings boiled in a
> sheet,
> Dandelion and crackies teeth, at the
> Killigrew's soiree.

Billy fished out his mouth organ and searched for the tune. It went with the frogs' evening song and the smell of wood smoke and high bush cranberries. Skipper kept dozing off. Midge disappeared under a culvert and didn't come out. Billy, still arguing with the tune, took no notice.

Skipper woke suddenly.

"Hark!" he said. "Hark to Midge!"

"Sounds like she's treed a squirrel," Billy said.

Skipper grabbed his telescope, dropped overboard, and raced as fast as his "rumatiks" would let him back along the road and down into the culvert. Billy reined in the team. Midge's racket stopped for a moment, and in the silence they heard a loud clanking sound. Presently, man and dog appeared above the bank. Skipper dragged a heavy chain attached to a vicious-toothed trap. The steel jaws were clamped around his precious telescope.

"I shoulda smelled that one sooner," he said. "Must have been dozing."

Billy gawped. "You can smell out traps!"

"Not as good as Midge," Skipper said. "Only sometimes she gets too anxious, like just now. I had to spring this one in a hurry or she'd been into it."

Billy's face slowly darkened with anger. "Why, that culvert's on *our* property," he said. "*Now* we'll see who's going to lay a charge against who." He cuffed Midge fondly and the dog grabbed his wrist between her jaws.

As soon as they reached home, Billy pried Skipper's glass loose. It was dented but it still worked all right. Then he took a sledge and hammered that trap into a mangled mess.

Toby's mother heard the whole story at dinner. Billy laughed more loudly than anyone when he came to the part about the *Nancy B* cruising along at four knots through a grain field . . . and the expression on Mr. Jenkins' face. Toby's mother couldn't help laughing herself and she said she never knew Billy had such a good sense of humor. Then she got out the fruitcake she saved for very special occasions. Billy had four pieces, not counting the one he sneaked under the table to Midge.

"Well," Billy said at last, "this isn't getting those cows milked."

Skipper excused himself and went into the parlor like he did every night to read the barometer.

Toby and his mother were clearing away the dishes when Billy opened the screen door and clanked the messed-up trap down on the wood box.

"You can wrap that up pretty," he said grimly, " 'cause I'm aimin' to give it to a fellow tomorrow . . . and Miz Ryner . . . should anyone try to tell you that old sea-farin' party is loony, you just remind him that so is a fox."

Farewell, Little Flying Squirrel
John Patrick Gillese

Peter, our pet flying squirrel, was born in the softwoods — on my father-in-law's farm, to be exact. Reconnoitering a ravine on a Sunday in June, our children saw a cat with what was left of Peter's mother. As soon as I had examined her (the kids wanted to know what kind of creature it was) I knew she was still feeding young. The children were anxious to find the den.

I suggested they look for an old poplar tree, preferably dead, with an abandoned woodpecker hole — the familiar dwelling place of the flying squirrel.

"Thump the trunk once, with the flat of your hand — like a flying squirrel landing. Then scratch with your fingernails."

It was a magic formula. When they found the right tree, almost instantly there was an answering scurrying from inside the trunk. A baby flying squirrel pushed its head through the opening: a living, pop-eyed little pixie of the softwood glades. Blinking against the light he emerged timidly, sure it was his mother that had made the landing noise.

Ever so carefully, one nature-starved boy climbed atop the shoulders of the other and tried to pluck the watchful little orphan from the hole of the tree. But despite hunger and heartache, the flying squirrel was filled with a sense of self preservation. Like a flash, it slipped around the trunk and down into the grasses. I'm sure it had seen its brothers and sisters, driven by hunger, leave like that before the boys came.

It was curiosity about the "nest" that led to the discovery of Peter, still inside, too timorous — perhaps too tiny — to clamber up to the opening. He was obviously the baby of the litter. The fur hadn't grown on his long flat tail. His rib cage was hammering from fear.

I tried to tell my sons that it is never wise to move a wilderness baby. Heartache alone can cause it to die. But they had one question I couldn't answer: how could this helpless one live when its mother would never return?

Peter came home in the car, held close to the finder's heart.

The children — five old enough to be fascinated; and little Thelma, too young for more than fragmentary flashes of interest — consulted in anxious agonies. How to feed Peter? Where to feed him? Where to keep him? Even as they talked, the boys were cleaning the hamster cage for a new home, the girls giving up a hitherto sacred doll bottle that Peter might eat.

They mixed sugar in milk, warmed it and tried it on their obliging baby sister. When little Thelma tilted the miniature milk bottle up in an effort to get a really decent swallow, they took it as a good sign. They washed the nipple under the tap — in case Peter got germs — then paraded in a group to the other baby, hidden in cottons in the hamster's old green cage.

Their patience was beyond belief. Like most parents, we were forever yelling at them not to slam doors and smash furniture. Their touch now was something to see: their fingers were rigid, for fear of holding Peter too tightly. For all that, the frightened, fear-sick flying squirrel wouldn't touch the milk.

The only hope I could proffer was that, as he became accustomed to the smell of their hands, hunger would make him try it.

Pat, the oldest, and the one claiming majority interest in Peter, fondled him for hours. He and Tim — next major shareholder in an orphaned flying squirrel — lay awake half the night, the cage strategically located between their beds, whispering and hoping.

They were falling asleep when they heard the stamping noise on the boards of the hamster cage. They didn't know it then, but this was the danger signal — the call of the baby flying squirrel when it is frightened and tries to summon its mother. Flying squirrels are nocturnal. With the darkness, the little one was hoping its mother would return.

Again the small stamping noise.

There is an empathy between human youngsters and others. Peter's mother could never come again. Instead, children's hands reached into the cage once more.

Next morning, Peter accepted a few drops of milk from the doll's bottle. There was jubilation even in the adult hearts.

I doubt if there is any living creature as gentle as the flying squirrel. Certainly there is none more shy. I was 18 before I saw my first little phantom of the northwoods, up in the Paddle River country of Alberta, where I had been trapping since boyhood.

One December evening, I stood in the soft blue dusk, resting before ascending the steep, scrub-covered hills to the uplands. Over the usual cries and calls of the wilderness, my ears had caught a new sound — a thumping in the spruce. Suddenly, between the sky and the hillside, I glimpsed a little ghost-body, arching down from a great bare balm, straight across a stretch of snowy river bend — a distance of fully 60 feet or so — and turning slightly upward as it approached another bare balm on the opposite bank. There was a soft *thuck* as it landed.

Soundless, I picked my way across the soft snowcover; but already the shy little squirrel had ascended to the top of the balm. I stood fully five minutes more before hearing the faint scratching — followed by the graceful glide across the snow-quilted river once more.

The zig-zag pattern indicated not only that the squirrel was getting breakfast — (his day begins when ours is ending) — but that he was having fun volplaning as well. A loose, black-edged membrane, lying in soft folds from wrist to ankle of the light body, makes it possible for the squirrel to glide a hundred feet or more. It does not really "fly", but it can twist, turn and bank in flight, using its featherweight tail as a rudder.

If the flying squirrel is shy, it has reason to be. Its enemies are legion — from the great horned owl, who also hunts by moonlight, to the arrogant red squirrel, who lives in similar haunts and, so outdoorsmen have assured me, is obsessed with a determination to emasculate the "greys". In my trapping days I even caught a few in sets laid for weasels. The fur was the softest, silkiest of any I ever handled — but too soft to have any commercial value.

No pet is more easily domesticated, none cleaner, none more possessive! As any other parent would, I dutifully observed the speed with which Peter attached himself to Pat and Tim — so much so that, by the time he was with us a week, he was rarely inside the hamster cage. That, in fact, caused the first commotion of fear.

There came a morning when the first sleepy-eyed boy made the pilgrimage to the cage, looked inside — and saw no Peter sleeping in his "bed" of doll clothes and warm cottons.

The yell of consternation brought four other children to the spot. Recrimination over who had failed to shut the door of the cage gave way to wild searching. (By now, however, the squirrel was as immune to child noises as is any old hound that's raised with half a dozen brothers.)

Dad had emerged the hero. I found the flying squirrel happily asleep in the boys' clothes-closet — in the pocket of a pair of jeans.

Peter permitted himself to be hugged and held, even "kissing" my wife on the lips in the gentlest of caresses, then went back to sleep — in the jeans.

By now Peter was the wonder not only of the community, but of two schools, junior and elementary. Visitors with uncombed hair and fearful skepticism on their faces came to see, and become flying squirrel disciples. Peter obligingly slept in the boys' jacket pockets in between "showings". He didn't like strangers, though, no matter how gentle. He would cling close to the boys' T-shirts; then, when whatever unduly alarmed him — a barking dog, for instance — was gone, he would climb up and murmur in their ears before slipping back into their pockets. Peter showed no partiality to either of the older boys, but preferred them, definitely, to the girls' company.

The empathy extended even to eating habits. (The only difference was that Peter liked good oatmeal porridge!) He ate everything the children or my wife offered him — raisins, pie, raspberries, sunflower seeds, nuts (only the best that money, earned from miles of pop-bottle hunting, could procure) cake and cookies. In true squirrel fashion, he hid much, especially great Brazil nuts and grapes. Even yet I sometimes take down a book from a high shelf in my study and behind it see a shrivelled little heap of food — a souvenir of Peter.

On this diet — or perhaps because of the more mystic food of love — Peter flourished. His coat grew sleek, his dark-fringed tail broadly resplendent. We were so much Peter's family by now that when he caught sight of himself in a dresser mirror, he turned in panic and came loping for the safety of our bodies!

Promptly after "waking" — around seven each evening — Peter groomed himself, smoothing his wrinkled fur, washing his body meticulously. Then came play! He would climb on somebody's shoulder, run around his neck (the tiny little claws never once scratching), peer over the other shoulder, nod, close his eyes, and jump — to whomever he had chosen to land on!

The children begged for Peter's favors. So, shamelessly, did the lady of our home. Surreptitiously at first, then with all pride gone, so did I.

Thelma was at the sitting-up-straight age then, able only to watch Peter in fascination, chortling in great glee when the other five squealed at his antics, waving fat baby arms in his direction.

One evening Peter slipped suddenly off Pat's T-shirt,

leaping like a ballet dancer for little Thelma's sitting-spot in the centre of the rug. Surrounded by cushions, she squealed her delight, reaching out fat baby fingers to catch him. She might as well have tried catching quicksilver or moonbeams.

Around and around her, seeming to float over her legs, with his tail lightly tickling her bare toes, Peter raced. Thelma laughed and laughed — almost helplessly. For both it became a daily game.

Peter seemed to understand that the boys — to whom he remained most attached — had to sleep during his "daytime". Periodically at night he would slip down the living room drapes (never "pulling" them, as a cat, for instance, may do when testing her claws), cross the floor, race up the stairs — a flying wraith — and ever so lightly touch the faces of those who had first "mothered" him. Thunder could not have wakened those growing boys, but Peter's gentle coaxing would bring a smile to their relaxed faces . . . their limp hands would wander in search of him. Content, he'd go back to his own pleasures.

With the advent of fall, Peter displayed more of the characteristics of his kind. He ate all the perishables now, porridge and milk in particular, but he stored nuts and raisins all over the house. He began shredding my books. I thought he craved something in his diet, or that his teeth were getting too long, but I am sure now it was an instinct to prepare a nest for winter, when the Canadian cold can be a bitter 60-below-zero.

And on a fall night, windy and cold, he found what his wild heart had never known before. The wind blew my study window open. Peter tasted the breath of frost-killed leaves in the ravines that run through our city. There was Virginia creeper on the side of the house, making descent simple — though all Peter had to do was stretch those silken membranes by his sides, and "fly".

In the morning he was gone.

I told the children he was too big, too smart, for any cat to get him. There were no owls, at least in the immediate vicinity. He might, I said, be anywhere nearby.

They looked at Dad with the same faith as when Dad told

them to tap a tree and a flying squirrel might appear, or look in the pocket of a pair of jeans and a little lost squirrel would be theirs again. It was hard to tell them that this time, Peter had undoubtedly headed for the ravine and the river and the wilds he could not even remember.

Hoping against hope, they searched the garage, the garden, the back alley, forlorn voices calling for a flying squirrel to come home. When we started them to school at last, they walked with an age that comes from something other than the passing years.

And I? Foolishly, when they were out of sight, I shook the Virginia creeper that hugged the house from basement to attic. I shook out sheltering sparrows and one astonished bat — but no Peter.

When my wife was busy in the basement with the wash, I climbed up to the attic, calling Peter by name. Then I went out to the garage, in case the kids had overlooked some new spot.

When I got back from the garage, my wife was also peering up into the thinning leaves of the Virginia creeper.

I like to think that within a few minutes after Peter left our home that windy autumn night, he was in the ravine, less than half-a-mile away . . . a place of sheltered softwoods and rose hips and shrivelled saskatoon berries . . . a place where even an inexperienced flying squirrel could spend the winter in safety. There, he and his kind can fill the woods with other little phantoms — those gentle wraiths of the evening called flying squirrels.

But there are times, when the children are asleep, and the maple outside our window makes a tacking sound on the roof, that my wife and I come breathlessly awake — sure we've heard the fairy-like patter of those wild and wonderful little feet again. Sentimental? Perhaps. But in the joy our family got from Peter, a richness came to all of us. It has something to do with family love — and whatever brings *that* into being, or makes it a little brighter, is surely priceless beyond compare.

Sport

Kirk Wirsig

A fisherman steps
to the banks of a river
a comfortable rainbow
lies still in the water
and slides to the surface
to dine on the hatches
the quick eye that follows
makes perfect the target
while seeking — mouth open
finds steel for its dinner
the stillness is broken
by ripples exploding
implacable bamboo
arcs out to the victim
but short is the battle
for scales are uneven
and mesh that is anxious
awaits gleaming silver
soon two pounds of muscle
lies dead in a basket
and fisherman heart-beats
are proud and disdainful
the womb of the mother
is spilled by the angler
and ten thousand children
lie dead on the sand.

The Encounter

Ivor Foster

The light early morning breeze gently parted the curtains of the bedroom window. Taking advantage of the momentary opening, a light beam found its way across the room to rest on the face of the sleeping boy.

The summer tan and the dark mop of hair stood out in stark contrast against the white pillow. Even asleep, the line of jaw and chin showed a certain strength of character, perhaps even stubbornness.

The boy's eyes opened moments before his mother's voice called from the bottom of the stairs, "David, it's time to get up."

He could hear her making breakfast in the kitchen as he dressed in clean jeans, white sweat shirt, socks and sneakers. Standing in front of the mirror, he looked at his image and ran his fingers through his tousled hair. This concession to good grooming out of the way, he grabbed a baseball cap from its perch atop the dresser mirror and jammed it firmly on his head. Throwing a light jacket over his shoulder he assaulted the sixteen steps of the stairway three at a time: a fourteen-year-old boy bent on adventure.

"Are you going to catch him today?" his mother asked as he sat down to the table, drinking his orange juice in the same motion. His answer was slowed by the quick demise of a glass of milk, Removing the ever-present cap, his mother set his plate of bacon, eggs and potatoes in front of him. "Don't know, Mom," he answered as he wiped away the remains of a white moustache with the back of his hand, "I might and I might not. If he's hungry I will. Looks good though," he said as he glanced out the window at the clear morning sky.

"Him" was a large hook-jawed male Brook trout that David called Whiteface. This unusual name was brought about by the presence of a large white scar on the left gill cover of the trout, evidence of an encounter with a larger fish some years before.

David remembered the first day he had encountered Whiteface. It was August and it was hot. He hadn't wanted to go fishing, but all the guys were busy at other things, so he went, thinking that at least it would be cooler by the creek. Even cooler than expected when he sat down (whether by accident or choice he couldn't remember) in the current of the "gravel hole" up to his neck. The heat also made it a poor day for fishing and by the time he reached the pool under the spruce he had caught only a bull, a rainbow and two brooks, all of them small.

At the upstream end of the pool were the remains of an old beaver dam over which the stream tumbled before coming to rest in the calmer waters of the pool below. The large spruce tree spread its protective and shady branches over the other side of the pool for nearly its entire length, making fishing from that side an impossibility. At the downstream end the water shallowed and made its way through a tangle of logs and debris, probably swept down from some long forgotten beaver dam farther upstream. On David's side, the pool was protected by a dense but not impenetrable thicket of willows, which grew from a bank at least five feet higher than the water below. The pool itself was shallow on the willow side but deeper (more than enough to keep a fish alive through the winter) under the spruce. The water had the color of weak tea, taken from the muskeg country through which it ran, but was crystal clear.

David had always known the hole was there, but the difficulty of getting to it had not made it one of his favorites. Sure, he had caught a few fish out of it, but only small ones (sometimes too small to keep) from the upstream end and always off casts which left little doubt that he did not want to lose a hook in the willow tangle or spruce branches overhead. Today though, even the small ones in the pool had stopped biting, and his enthusiasm didn't improve when he tore a hole in his shirt clambering up the tangled face of the dam from his water soaked and frustrating perch below.

Looking for some shade, he found a natural tunnel through the willows which led him to an opening above the middle of the pool. The spruce branches were higher at this point and it was evident that the pool on that side was even deeper than he first thought. Peering down into the deeper area beneath the spruce, David's eye caught a movement. "Only a weed waving in the current," he thought, but his attention was quickly brought back to the "weed" which this time moved toward him in the current. Immediately he knew it was a trout, and bigger than any he had caught before. From David's vantage point, the fish appeared to be at least three pounds and a good sixteen inches long. David stared at the fish in open-mouthed astonishment for a few moments, then with his heart thumping in his chest, he backed out of the willows to retrieve his rod. Hands shaking, he baited his hook with the biggest grasshopper in his bait can.

Retracing his path, David looked down to find the trout still there. Very carefully he eased his old telescopic rod out over the water. When all seven feet were fully extended, he gently released the line held in his left hand. The weight of the grasshopper and sinker pulled the loose folds of line through the rod guides. A slight touch on the line and the grasshopper disappeared beneath the surface without a splash. The fish, which David could still see, began to move toward the bait. As it did, David jiggled the rod tip a few times. The trout shot forward, grabbed the grasshopper, turned and headed toward the far bank. Before he reached it David set the hook, abruptly stopping the forward progress of the fish. Having little room to manoeuvre, David dropped the rod, grabbed the line and began hauling the fighting fish in hand over hand.

Dragging the trout through the willows extending over the bank proved to be his undoing. The line became entangled and the fish broke free before David could get his hand close enough to grasp it. As the fish flopped in the shallow water at the foot of the bank, David could see the crimson lines on the fins, the prominent hook in the lower jaw and the worm-like markings on its dark green back. The orange and red speckled sides gleamed as the powerful square tail of the fish got a bite in the water, which sent it rocketing back into the safety of the deep hole beneath the spruce. Before it disappeared David saw a large white mark on the gill cover of the fish.

"Man, what a fish!" David thought to himself, as his shaking hands untangled his line. "I'm going to catch that fish . . ."

David could no longer remember when he had begun to think of the fish as Whiteface, probably while recounting the adventure to his mother, but the fish soon became an obsession with him. Summer passed into fall and golden leaves soon gave way to winter and still he had not caught Whiteface. During the winter he spent hours poring over old and new copies of *Outdoor Life, Fisherman,* and other outdoor magazines. He read books on fishing until he felt he knew more about Whiteface than the fish did himself. He checked and rechecked his fishing equipment until his mother felt he would have it worn out. Many times that winter his teachers caught him day dreaming and had to bring him back with a sharp word. Spring came, spring floods eased and the streams cleared up for another summer. Even before school was out David spent every available moment at the spruce hole trying to tempt Whiteface with every trick he could think of, but to no avail. He did hook him again, twice in fact, but only lightly, otherwise the fish turned down every offering, after looking it over carefully in taunting fashion, before melting back into the dark water under the spruce.

One day while lying in his usual spot, David flipped a dead grasshopper from his bottle into the faster water at the head of the pool. Moments later he was mildly surprised to see the torpedo shape of Whiteface rise to the surface of the pool, suck in the floating insect and return to his hideaway. David quickly threw another grasshopper, this time alive, onto the surface of the pool. Again Whiteface responded, even more eagerly, shattering the calm of the surface, before returning to a spot near the middle of the pool where David could still see him. Hurriedly, he removed the sinker from his line and baited up with a fresh grasshopper. In his haste to get his rod out over the water, he banged it against a willow branch. In a flash, Whiteface was gone.

When David's grasshopper had floated the length of the pool twice, with no results, he knew it was no use. At least not today, but he had the secret now.

"That was last week," David thought as he said goodbye to his mother and picked up his equipment from the back porch. The past week had been pure agony. Cutting lawns, rain and running errands had kept him from any idea of fishing.

An hour later, he was at his usual vantage point gazing down into "the spruce hole", searching for some sign of Whiteface. His eyes picked out a faint movement, and as they became used to the dark water, he could pick out the outline of the fish. Almost as if he knew David was there, Whiteface moved out of the shadow and waited.

Shaking hands carefully eased the fully extended rod out over the water. With a slight flip of the rod tip the grasshopper was propelled upstream into the waiting water. Seconds later the kicking grasshopper floated into the calm waters of the pool.

As soon as he saw it, Whiteface rose in a welter of foam and the grasshopper vanished from the surface. As the fish turned back to his place on the bottom of the pool, David, in calm determination, set the hook.

The sting of the needle-sharp point sent Whiteface into a frenzy and he tore up and down the pool, once almost getting the line tangled in some underwater debris. David, not repeating the mistakes of their first encounter, simply raised the rod tip and snubbed him away from this obstruction. Once he sulked in mule fashion on the bottom and David only got him moving again by rapping the rod butt with his knuckles. Hours later, or so it seemed to David, Whiteface was showing signs of tiring. His runs were not so long and the power was gone from his frantic lunges.

Soon the fish was floating on his side on the surface of the pool. Holding his rod in his right hand, the rod tip maintaining tension on the line, David eased himself over the edge of the bank until he was clear of the willows and standing in the shallow water below. Watching the fish for any signs of renewed fight, he waded upstream and eventually reached the spray-soaked patch of flat ground below the dam. From there it was a simple matter of sliding the exhausted fish onto the wet grass at his feet.

Kneeling down, unaware that he was getting wet, David was able to make out clearly the scar that gave the fish its name. It stood out in stark contrast to the dark head and vibrant colors of the rest of the fish.

A sudden thought crossed David's mind as he remembered all the times he had watched the fish in his hole. The contest had been between him and Whiteface. No one else knew except his mother and now he had won. Somehow he knew, the victory would be for nothing if he kept the fish.

Wetting his hands, David picked up the fish, removed the hook from its mouth and waded into the water. Holding Whiteface in both hands beneath the surface, David gently moved him back and forth until he could feel the fish move in his grip. When the fish was able to move on his own, he released him and stepped back.

Whiteface lay there for a moment, gathering strength, then with a slow beat of his fins, almost in salute, he moved out into the current and disappeared in the shadow beneath the spruce.

The Guide Knows Everything

N. Vernon-Wood

Three-four years ago, the Trail Riders of the Canadian Rockies had a picture in their bulletin that shure give us local dude wranglers a kick. It's a photo of old Bill Slaney conversin' with a bevy of sweet young she-Pilgrims. The old side-hill gouger is looking plumb intelligent (for him), an' it's titled "The Guide Knows Everything".

Which same is undoubtedly what some Pilgrims seem to expect. A man's got to know the country, an' how to make a comfortable camp. He has to be able to shoe a cayuse, patch a tent, swing an ax, an' build a decent meal; an' when he can do them he's only just started. He mighty soon discovers that he also has to be a naturalist, geologist, an' botanist, besides a jack-knife surgeon, a recontoor, a ballistics expert, an' a pretty fair judge of human nature an' how much exposure to give a fillum on a dull day.

An' every once in a while some bird will pull something like this: "Look at that view, Tex; don't you think Corot would have loved to paint it, or do you think Browning would have caught the atmosphere better — or do you?"

When they start that sort of thing, it's a good plan to grab your field glasses plumb excited an' say, "Holy old doodle, they's a bear on that slide — no, b'gosh, it's a burned stump. Don't it beat hell how them shadders fool you sometimes?"

All this here preamble is by way of explainin' why it is a feller's apt to get him what the experts call a Complex. He gets so he begins to think he just about does know it all, an' just then somethin' sneaks up an' busts his little pink balloon all to hell.

Take trout fishin', f'rinstance. I'm what you might call a fair-to-middlin' journeyman angler, but most of my stream whippin' has been done for strictly utilitarian purposes, fish in the pan bein' the prime motive, an' I've never branched out into the finer an' more artistic aspects of the sport. But that don't prevent me recognizin' an' appreciatin' a top hand when I see one. An' Father Moriarty was one of 'em. He's the priest in charge of the Bankhead Mission, an' shepherd to the wildest flock of woolies that ever cracked a prayer-book.

I'm comin' down Johnson Canyon, onetime, an' down at the bottom of a cliff, in a scrub spruce, I find a hummin'-bird's nest — one of them delicate bits of ornithological construction that makes a man feel clumsy as an ox, just to look at. I meet up with this Padre, who has a camera an' fishin' rod along with him, so I ask does he want to make a picture of the nest, with a cute ruby-throat settin' on a couple of pea-sized eggs. Right away he got human, an' we scrambled back together.

From bird's-nesting with a camera we naturally got on to fishin', an' I took the old feller to the pool at the foot of the falls. That hole was one of the major blights in my comparatively carefree existence. It's full of rainbow trout as big as pack horses, almost, an' are they snooty? I've tried 'em with Royal Coachmen, Brown Hackles, an' Black Gnats accordin' to season an' weather conditions. I've used Bucktails, Colorado Spinners, Rubber Grasshoppers, an' God help me, worms. The mornin' sun has risen on my shiverin' form, up to my pants pockets in the icy water, tryin' to inviggle them blasted 'bows to strike, an' it's gone down behind Sawback Peak throwin' its last crimson beam on a disgruntled waddy still feebly castin' along the edge of the riffles. An' all I ever took out of there was half a dozen tiddlers that was too immature to know better.

I led his Reverence to that hole with malice aforethought. I'd got the notion that if I couldn't catch them trout, no one could — same bein' a typical example of Guide Philosophy.

His eyes kind of lit up when we looked down into the drink, an' he says, "What do you suggest we use?"

"Well," I tell him, "I think I'll try a Wickham's Fancy as a dropper, an' a Gnat for point. What flies you got?"

"I think I'll just sit and watch a while. I'm not as young as I was, and a rest seems to be indicated."

So I unwound a leader from my hat, an' unlimbered my rod. I've got to let on that I really believe them pediculous pink-bellies are takeable, but it's just a gesture as far's I'm concerned. The Father sat him on a rock, an' seemed about as interested as a river hog at a ladies' quiltin' bee. After I'd made forty-'leven fruitless casts, he pulled a mess of feathers, yarn, horsehair, an' old socks out of his pocket, an' opened a tin that had originally contained half a pound of Dublin Shag. Out came a few hooks, a pair of scissors, an' he went to work.

A few minutes later, he stepped up alongside an' laid seventy foot of line across that pool in a manner that was a joy to see. He's usin' only one fly, an' it lit like thistle-down on the lee side of a big rock that stuck out where the water boiled after plunging over the falls.

Just as he recovered, I thought I seen a shadowy shape rise, an' on the next cast I knew it. It come up from behind that rock, an' struck like the trip-hammers of hell. An' I stood an' watched a paunchy little priest handle six an' one-half pounds of wet dynamite an' lightnin' with a four-ounce rod in a manner that got me thinkin' of D'Artagnan, an' the swordsman's wrist. What's more, I found out later he uses a leader like cobweb.

That little man could sit on the bank of a stream, study the water, weather, an' the insect life, an' then take somethin' from his fly-book that would look to those trout the way fresh-broiled deer liver looks to a hungry Pilgrim. I got so I invented jobs over to Bankhead on the off chance of runnin' into Father Moriarty an' persuadin' him to play hookey. I've seen him catch trout where there wasn't any, an' I never seen him lift more'n two out of the water in any one day. He'd bring 'em to the shallows, slip his fingers down the line, an' takin' care his hand was wet, slip out his hook gentle as a woman. "There you are," he'd say. "Back to your pet eddy, an' meditate on the sin of gluttony, an' next time, don't mistake the shadow for the substance."

They buried the Father last fall. From the cemetery here, you can hear the Bow falls roarin' loud an' deep in the spring, an' sort of musical the rest of the time, so his body is right handy to good trout water, an' I'll bet you four bits that his spirit is havin' one whale of a time with them other sportsmen, the Galilee fishermen, Ike Walton, an' Grey of Falloden.

Last fall, havin' nothin' much to do, an' a month to do it in, I says to the youngest of my quiverful, "Want to skip school an' come along with me while I see can we get the odd elk for eatin' purposes, son?"

Which is Unnecessary Question No. 59. So we pack a couple of cayuses an' hit south. Three days' travel puts us at the foot of a pass that divides Alberta from British Columbia, an' is the watershed between the Saskatchewan an' Columbia river systems. The B.C. side is crummy with elk, an' there's bear on both slopes. We fixed up camp for a week's stay, an' next mornin' headed up the pass afoot. Before we'd gone three miles, we'd spotted nine bulls, mostly young stuff, an' all easy pickin's.

The kid wanted we should bust the first one we seen, but I thought this was as good a time as any to inculcate a little hunter's patience into his system.

"No hurry, son; never grab the first thing you see, when you might get just what you want later."

Couple of hours after, we spotted a twelve-pointer 'way up on a slide, so we made a stalk, an' laid him out. I grallocked him, an' takin' only the liver for immediate consumption, hung my old sweater on his antlers to flag off the prowlin' coyote, an' we backtracked for camp.

The Guide Knows Everything   157

While we're fryin' up some liver next mornin', the youngster wants to know was there any trout in the crick that wandered by camp.

"Search me, son," I says, "but I doubt it. It's a right pifflin' watercourse, an' I never took the trouble to wet a line in it. Still an' all, trout, like gold, are where you find 'em. Want to take a whirl at it?"

He opined he might, so I tell him to get the tackle an' go to it, while I salvage the meat. I figger it's a good way to keep him occupied while I tend to the serious business of life. What with this an' that, I don't get back till mid-afternoon. There's no sign of his Nibs in camp, so after hanging the plunder over a smudge to discourage the flies, I wander downstream to see has a grizzly spooked him into a tree, or is he asleep on the bank.

Half a mile below camp, I meet him ploddin' along. Ploddin' is right! He's wet, cold, an' hungry, but is he downhearted? The peaks echo "*no!*" The little sonofagun has a mess of cutthroat, runnin' from four to six pounds apiece, that any man would be proud of.

After we'd fed our faces, an' admired them trout some, he says, "Dad, did you know there was a trout like that in this crick?"

"Son, I didn't know they was anything more than frogs, an' that's a fact."

He gives me one of them long, cold looks that kids can turn on so good. "Heck," he says, "I thought you guides knowed everythin'."

The White Buffalo

D. P. Barnhouse

This is an incident told by an old man of the Stoney Indian tribe of Southern Alberta.

The RCMP came west in 1874 to control the unscrupulous whisky traders, following the savage violence at Fort Whoop-Up, and to try to control the wasteful slaughter of the buffalo herds for the hides alone.

The river quickened as it neared the island. Johnny Kildeer strained at the paddle, eyes alert for the white water which warned of hidden rocks.

His battle with the current made him forget some of his resentment of the old medicine man who sat in the bow with "Small Dog" pressed against his knees. Louis Three Thumbs was pretending to doze, but Johnny knew that his narrowed gaze measured every swirl of water and that under the blanket his own paddle was held at the ready.

He was a great hunter once, Johnny thought, and a powerful voice among the Blackfeet. But he had begun to change — perhaps even before the praying men came. They were the white men who spoke of Christian brotherhood and who put great value upon men's souls.

But before that there were others who put even greater value on the hides of buffalo. These were the whisky traders who came in great wagons full of "fire in bottles" and who had burned whole villages in the southern hills.

The young braves found it more exciting to wallow in the blood of animals and the white man's fire water than to listen to the sober warnings of praying men. So they laughed and turned away, but the old ones listened. Louis Three Thumbs soon began to talk like the praying men. He spoke of the iron horse that would bring many settlers and many changes to the plains;

of ploughing the earth and of planting seeds; of putting down roots into the soil that would be there even after the herds were gone.

Soon the braves laughed at him as well and Johnny felt both angry and ashamed. Hadn't Louis Three Thumbs once pitted his medicine against the whole tribe to save one small Cree captive? Since it was Johnny Kildeer whose life had been spared he felt alternately angry at Louis for letting his power slip away and at the braves for making fun of him.

"Old man's courage is locked up in mission house," they scoffed. "Let white man teach prairie dog to burrow in earth, but not our people."

Louis still made medicine for his tribe, but small medicine now. Each autumn Johnny helped him gather roots and bark to heal wounds and to soothe fever.

On Frog Island grew a certain yellow flower in great profusion. Johnny enjoyed this trip down river — the night on the island, the long pull back upstream. But not this time, for the traders had come again. The braves were gone on the trail of buffalo, and how Johnny had longed to go with them! The envy that stung his heart now poisoned his tongue.

"Why do you let them call you 'Old Mother Partridge'?" he asked Louis suddenly, knowing the words would sting.

"Scorn makes the best stopper for ears which will not hear the truth," the old man said.

"When I was small you went always with them on the hunt."

"True. I study earth and water hole and the way the wind blows till we find the herd — but not for whisky trader. He is like disease spreading white bones over the face of the prairie — disease no medicine can cure."

"But the braves say that buffalo are many, like hairs on a man's head."

"White man's rifle soon thin hairs on scalp. Then when buffalo go, Indians go."

160 WildLife?

"Shall I never be a hunter, then? Am I always to be a digger of roots, like you?"

Louis said nothing for a moment. Then he spat into the swirling water.

"No honest hunt any more," he said. "In old days, bow and arrow kill for food; fur for blanket; hide for tepee; bone for needle; sinew for bowstring, for thread . . . all used up and nothing left to rot in sun. Now braves kill, kill, kill only for skin. Skin for white man; carcass for crows, for flies. Soon nothing left for Indian."

After this outburst, unusually long and angry for the old man, he wrapped himself once more in silence. They rounded a bend and the river deepened, dropped over a series of riffles. At this time of year when the water was low a man could wade to the island from either bank if he could hold his footing in the swift current.

The sun began to go down and a chill breeze took its place. Johnny strained his eyes against the gathering dusk. As they neared the island they smelled the smoke of campfires. Up on the flatlands a mile or so downstream, white plumes rose against the fiery sunset. Johnny looked toward them with longing as he slid the canoe's nose up on the stony beach.

"The hunt is over," Louis said. "They have made camp."

Small Dog jumped ashore first. He bounded through the tall sedges, rolled joyously in sand pockets. Then, nose to the ground, he worked his way through the scrub willow which grew thick and tangled over most of the island.

"He smells game," Louis said. "Ah, it is good to stretch the legs!" He wandered off after Small Dog.

Johnny gazed a long time down river toward the camp fires. Snatches of songs and shouting drifted down from the flatlands. They must have had a good kill. The women would be busy with the skinning knives now and the white traders would be greedily counting hides. He gathered some driftwood for a fire and was bending over it when he heard a low whistle. He whirled to see Louis Three Thumbs beckoning from the underbrush. In spite of the gathering darkness, Johnny could sense that something unusual had happened.

Something in the old man's manner told Johnny to tread softly. He waded through the coarse knee-high grasses to where the trees began. Louis' hand gripped his arm and drew him into the thicket. They worked their way carefully over deadfall and through tangled branches. There was no trail but the old man stopped every now and then to listen. Suddenly they heard Small Dog whine softly.

"He has a good nose," Louis whispered. "Look there!" He pointed to a dark patch ahead where bent trees formed a sort of cave. A silvery shape moved slightly in the shadows. "A buffalo calf — come here for safety."

"It's . . . it's white," Johnny breathed. His voice was full of wonder. He'd heard the braves talk of white buffalo, a freak of nature, rarely seen. No Blackfoot had ever taken one. Of that he was sure. The traders would pay much for that one.

The ungainly calf stood facing them. The great dark eyes were wells full of unknown terror. Small Dog growled and the massive head went down in the age-old gesture of defiance.

"Is he not beautiful?" the old man said, "and strange, like the ghost of his race . . . perhaps an omen."

Johnny began to move slowly backward the way they had come. "Watch him till I come back," he ordered Small Dog. When he had gone a few yards he turned and ran as fast as he could through the tangle.

His hunting knife was still lying where he'd been cutting chips for the fire. He was honing the blade on a rock when Louis came out of the tall grass and stood beside him.

"What is in your mind, my son?"

"I will have his hide," Johnny said, thinking of the envious eyes of the braves.

"It is a legend of our people," Louis said, "that the eye which feasts on one of these pale ones feasts long on life. He has escaped the guns of the hunters. When he has rested he will find the herd again. Why would you kill him?"

"I will have his hide," Johnny repeated stubbornly. "To have taken a white buffalo will make me a big man in the tribe."

"Look," Louis said, pointing to the distant fires. "Up there lie many of his brothers for the crows to pick tomorrow. They lie thick like fires on the torn earth. Is there need of meat? They will take the tongues for feasting but there will be no making of pemmican. We become too lazy, for with guns it is easier to kill again; to kill a beast for its tongue and for its skin which the white traders will take away. This is the work of braves who are no longer brave — only foolish."

"They have taken many," Johnny said, "but they have not taken a white one." He tested the blade on his thumb and got up to go.

"Wait!" Louis said, and took the knife from his hand in one swift movement.

"Give me back my knife. I cannot kill with my bare hands."

"Think well, my son. You alone of the Cree prisoners were spared. Is this not so?"

"It is so, and I know that it was because of you. Your medicine was big then and they dared not go against you."

"So," Louis said, "let us try small medicine now." He grasped the knife by its point and sent it spinning high into the air. "Blade to buffalo calf, him die . . . hilt to calf, him live. We let knife speak."

The knife came down in a flittering arc. The blade struck sparks from the white pebbles, bounced off a large rock, skimmed like a flat stone out over the water and disappeared beneath the surface. Johnny stared at the swiftly flowing stream.

"Your medicine is no good any more, old man. I will fetch the hunters. They will help me kill the calf." They looked at each other for a moment without speaking. Then Johnny Kildeer turned to go. The old man took his own knife from its sheath and held it out.

"Very well, my son. You are like the shrew who goes blindly in the dark. Take my knife and when you drive it home remember you strike also at your people. Do it so . . . swiftly." He bent over the fire, turning his back on Johnny.

Small Dog still held the calf at bay. Johnny approached warily. He pointed the blade of his knife the way Louis Three Thumbs had shown him, and moved closer. The head lowered and the dark, terrified eyes looked up at him. They gazed at each other as he and Louis had done a few minutes before, each waiting for the other to move. Johnny remembered himself, a Cree child, standing alone among the Blackfeet, and he felt the strength ooze out of his arm. His knife blade shone in the half light. Small Dog crept against his feet, whining for instructions. The white calf stood unmoving — like a pale ghost in the thicket.

Suddenly he knew he didn't wish to see that white hide stained red with blood. He put the knife in his belt and turned away. Small Dog followed without protest. Johnny looked back once at the white blur in the dark thicket.

"Rest well, little pale one," he wished silently, "and travel swiftly till you find the herd."

A rising wind stirred the willows and pressed waves into the long grass. He smelled the smoke of Louis' campfire. He was suddenly very hungry. They would sleep under the stars and tomorrow he and Louis Three Thumbs would gather many roots for medicine to heal the sick.

For Joe MacKinaw

Jim Dumont

In my youth
I went south,
In my dreams
I went south.

There
I watched them hunt . . .
I watched them hunt the buffalo.
And in my heart
I hunted with them.

Now they are gone.
The buffalo have left,
Ashamed,
That we had let them die,
Mercilessly,
At the hand of the white hunters.

But our real suffering
Has not yet come upon us.
Soon there will be great destruction.
Fire will cover the whole land.
We will be punished.

This is the truth;
There will be much suffering.
The old people tell us that:
The Great Spirit has talked with them.
The old people know;
There has been too much evil.

Yet there is a little hope,
The Great Spirit makes room for goodness.

A young boy will come
The old people say,
And he will lead those who know goodness;
He will lead them into the mountains
No whiteman has been there;
No whiteman knows;
Destruction will not be allowed there;
And there is the sanctuary for goodness.

. . . in my old age
I will go in dreams
And I will find the buffalo again.

The "Wars" of the Eighties and Nineties (1882-1900)
J. W. Chafe

Many people today still remember their grandparents reminiscing about the "old days", when people were irrepressibly lighthearted in facing the hardships of frontier life. So they were, of course; but there was conflict aplenty, especially in a new country where new relationships had to be worked out. So inevitably, there were many clashes between competing interests: "Wars" of one kind or another were being waged all the time.

One of these "wars" was not against people, but against the buffalo, which was eventually exterminated. Not by the Indians; they hardly made a dent in their vast numbers. Nor even by the Métis. The disappearance of the buffalo was probably due, to a large extent, to the American railways, which kept gangs of sharpshooters systematically slaughtering them; Buffalo Bill is said to have once shot sixty a minute for almost an hour. One scientist feels that the terrible blizzards and deep snow of

1880-81 might have had much to do with finishing them off. In 1880, there were still large numbers: by 1882, there were only a scattered few.

A tragedy to the Indian! For the hunter of the plains the great beast had provided not just pemmican but every necessity of life. Its skin made his tepee and his coat, his bridle and his lariat; it even served as a boat for crossing streams — when stretched on a hoop made of willows. He used its horns for a powder-flask and its sinews for bow-strings. The buffalo robe had been his carpet and his bed in life, and his shroud in death. Now the Indian, riding listlessly over the plains, would see only bleaching bones. A few years later he would see the white man's "iron horse" pulling carloads of bones to Chicago to be used in the bleaching of sugar and making of fertilizer. The old order had indeed changed.

If there are thousands of buffalo in parks all over the continent today — so many that they have to be thinned out occasionally — it is because a few men were farsighted enough to save a small number of calves. James Mackay was one of them; he brought eight calves to his farm at Deer Lodge and allowed them to pasture with his cattle. Years later, stockmen in Canada and the United States bred buffalo to domestic cattle, hoping to produce a hardier breed of beef cow. They got a hybrid they called a "cattalo"; then found that the males were always sterile. Buffalo meat, which sustained generations of fur traders and *voyageurs,* is still served on special occasions. Recently the University of Manitoba's football team, the Bisons, served "bisonburgers" to a visiting American team.

The Red River Buffalo Hunt

Alexander Ross

The Red River Buffalo hunt was unique in North America. In the story of the westward march of civilization across the continent no other people organized themselves so efficiently and so extensively for a systematic assault on the buffalo herds.

These large organized hunts began in the early 1820s and continued until the early 1870s, though with gradually diminishing enthusiasm and extent as the herds dwindled and withdrew farther and farther westward. Probably no comparable community depended for so long a time and to such an extent on the "plains provisions" which the great hunts provided.

This excerpt, taken from "Red River Settlement", is of the spring hunt of 1840. At this time the importance of the buffalo to the economy of Red River would be hard to exaggerate. Though this account is of particular events which the writer witnessed, everything that he tells us may be considered typical of most of the great hunts.

. . . "On the 15th of June, 1840, carts were seen to emerge from every nook and corner of the settlement bound for the plains . . . From Fort Garry the cavalcade and camp-followers went crowding on to the public road, and thence, stretching from point to point, till the third day in the evening, when they reached Pembina, the great rendezvous on such occasions . . . Here the roll was called, and general muster taken, when they numbered, on this occasion, 1,630 souls; and here the rules and regulations for the journey were finally settled. The officials for the trip were named and installed into office; and all without the aid of writing materials.

The camp occupied as much ground as a modern city, and was formed in a circle; all the carts were placed side by side, the trams outward. These are trifles, yet they are important to our subject. Within this line of circumvallation, the tents were placed in double, treble rows, at one end; the animals at the other in front of the tents. This is in order in all dangerous places; but where no danger is apprehended, the animals are kept on the outside. Thus the carts formed a strong barrier, not only for securing the people and their animals within, but as a place of shelter against an attack of the enemy without.

In 1820, the number of carts assembled here for the first trip was 540; in 1825, 680; in 1830, 820; in 1835, 970; in 1840, 1,210.

From this statement it is evident that the plain hunters are rapidly increasing. . . . The first step was to hold a council for the nomination of chiefs or officers, for conducting the expedition. Ten captains were named, the senior on this occasion being Jean Baptiste Wilkie, an English Métis, brought up among the French; a man of good sound sense and long experience, and withal a fine bold-looking and discreet fellow; a second Nimrod in his way. Besides being captain, in common with the others, he was styled the great war chief or head of the camp; and on all public occasions he occupied the place of president. All articles of property found, without an owner, were carried to him, and he disposed of them by crier, who went around the camp every evening, were it only an awl. Each captain had ten soldiers under his orders; in much the same way that policemen are subject to the magistrate. Ten guides were likewise appointed; their duties were to guide the camp, each in his turn — that is day about — during the expedition. The camp flag belongs to the guide of the day; he is therefore standard-bearer in virtue of his office.

The raising of the flag every morning is the signal for raising camp. Half an hour is the full time allowed to prepare for the march; but if any one is sick, or their animals have strayed, notice is sent to the guide, who halts till all is made right. From the time the flag is hoisted, however, till the hour of camping arrives, it is never taken down. The flag taken down is the signal for encamping. While it is up, the guide is chief of the expedition. Captains are subject to him, and the soldiers' duties commence. They point out the order of the camp, and every cart, as it arrives, moves to its appointed place. This business usually occupies about the same time as raising camp in the morning; for everything moves with the regularity of clockwork.

All being ready to leave Pembina, the captain and other chief men hold another council, and lay down the rules to be observed during the expedition. Those made on the present occasion were:

1. No buffalo to be run on the Sabbath-day.
2. No party to fork off, lag behind, or go before, without permission.
3. No person or party to run buffalo before the general order.
4. Every captain with his men, in turn, to patrol the camp, and keep guard.
5. For the first trespass against these laws, the offender to have his saddle and bridle cut up.
6. For the second offence, the coat to be taken off the offender's back, and be cut up.
7. For the third offence, the offender to be flogged.
8. Any person convicted of theft, even to the value of a sinew, to be brought to the middle of the camp, and the crier to call out his or her name three times, adding the word "Thief", at each time.

Not to dwell on the ordinary routine of each day's journey, it was the ninth day from Pembina before we reached the Chienne River, distance only about 150 miles; and as yet we had not seen a single band of buffalo. On the third of July, our nineteenth day from the settlement, and at a distance of little more than 250 miles, we came in sight of our destined hunting ground; and on the day following, as if to celebrate the anniversary of American Independence, we had our first buffalo race. Our array in the field must have been a grand and imposing one to those who have never seen the like before. No less than 400 huntsmen, all mounted and anxiously waiting for the word "Start!" took up their position in a line at one end of the camp, while Captain Wilkie, with his spyglass at his eye surveyed the buffalo, examined the ground, and issued his orders. At 8 o'clock the whole cavalcade broke ground, and made for the buffalo; first at a slow trot, then at a gallop, and lastly at full speed. Their advance was over a dead level, the plain having no hollow or shelter of any kind to conceal their approach. We need not answer any queries as to the feeling and anxiety of the camp on such an occasion. When the horsemen started, the cattle might have been a mile and half ahead; but they had approached to within four or five hundred yards before the bulls curved their tails or pawed the ground. In a moment more the herd took flight, and horse and rider are presently seen bursting in among them; shots are heard, and all is smoke, dust, and hurry. The fattest are first singled out for slaughter; and in less time than we have occupied with the description, a thousand carcasses strew the plain.

Those who have seen a squadron of horses dash into battle, may imagine the scene, which we have no skill to depict. The earth seemed to tremble when the horses started; but when the animals fled, it was like the shock of an earthquake. The air was darkened; the rapid firing at first, soon became more and more faint, and at last died away in the distance. Two hours, and all was over; but several hours more elapsed before the result was known, or the hunters reassembled; and who is he so devoid of feeling and curiosity that could not listen to a detail of the perilous adventure.

The moment the animals take to flight, the best runners dart forward in advance. At this moment a good horse is invaluable to his owner; for out of the four hundred on this occasion, not above fifty got the first chance of the fat cows. A good horse and experienced rider will select and kill from ten to twelve animals at one heat, while inferior horses are contented with two or three; but much depends on the nature of the ground. On this occasion, the surface was rocky and full of badger holes. Twenty-three horses and riders were at one moment all sprawling on the ground, one horse, gored by a bull, was killed on the spot, two more disabled by the fall. One rider broke his shoulder-blade; another burst his gun, and lost three of his fingers by the accident and a third was struck on the knee by an exhausted bullet. These accidents will not be thought over numerous, considering the result; for in the evening no less than 1,375 tongues were brought into camp.

The rider of a good horse seldom fires till within three or four yards of his object, and never misses; and, what is admirable in point of training, the moment the shot is fired, his steed springs on one side to avoid stumbling over the animal; whereas an awkward and shy horse will not approach within ten or fifteen yards, consequently the rider has often to fire at random, and not infrequently misses; many of them, however, will fire at double that distance, and make sure of every shot. The mouth is always full of bullets. They load and fire at the gallop, and but seldom drop a mark, although some do to designate the animal.

When the runners leave the camp, the carts prepare to follow to bring in the meat. The carters have a bewildering task to perform; they have to make their way through a forest of carcasses, till each finds out his own. The pursuit is no sooner over than the hunter, with coat off and shirt sleeves tucked up, commences skinning and cutting up the meat; with the knife in one hand, the bridle hanging in the other, and the loaded gun close by, he from time to time casts a wistful look around, to see that no lurking enemy is at hand watching for the opportunity to take a scalp. The hunter's work is now retrograde; the last animal killed is the first skinned, and night, not infrequently, surprises him at his work; what then remains is lost, and falls to the wolves; hundreds of animals are sometimes abandoned, for even a thunderstorm, in one hour, will render the meat useless. The day of a race is as fatiguing for the hunter as the horse; but the meat once in the camp, he enjoys the very luxury of idleness. Then the task of the women begins, who do all the rest; and what with skins, and meat, and aft, their duty is a most laborious one." . . .

The Last Husky
Farley Mowat

So the people built the little igloo and departed into the wastelands. They went from the place singing the laments for the dying, and they left nothing behind them except the old man. They even took Arnuk, the dog, for that was the old man's wish, and Arnuk was the last and most precious gift that an old man could make to his son and to his grandson and to his people.

It had been a bitter season; the long hungry months before the spring, and in the camp of the people there had been endless cries of children who were too young to know that starvation must be faced in silence. There had been death in the camp, not of men, but of those who were almost as important to the continuance of human life. For the dogs had died, one by one, and as each one was stilled in death so did man's hopes for the future shrink. For in the stark plains country of the Barrenlands men and dogs are one in their need for each other.

Yet though it had been a bitter time, there had been no word spoken against the folly of feeding one old and useless human body. Maktuk, the son, had shared his own meagre rations equally between his aged father, and his starving child who also bore the name that linked the three together. No word was ever spoken, but on a dark April day, the old man raised himself slowly from the sleeping ledge and gazed for a little while at his grandchild, and out of the depths of a great love, and greater courage, old Maktuk spoke these words.

"I have it in my heart," he said, "that the deer await you at the Western Lakes. Go quickly to them, else you will remain in this empty place forever. Go when morning comes, and I will stay. And you shall take Arnuk with you that in the years ahead you will remember me and not forget to leave the spirit gifts upon my grave."

There had been no discussion and no argument, for even an old man has his rights, and this is his final one. In the morning the people were gone, and behind young Maktuk's sled the dog Arnuk tugged convulsively at her tether and turned her head backward to the small white mound of the abandoned igloo, rising shadowless against the endless snows.

Arnuk had been born in the preceding spring in the lean times that always grip the land before the deer return. She was the seventh pup of the litter, and there was no food for her. And if an old man had not taken it upon himself to feed and care for her, she would have died before her life began. Yet she saw summer come and knew the pleasures of long days spent romping with the other young dogs by the side of the great river where the summer camp was pitched. When she grew tired, she would come to the skin tent and push against the old man's knees until he opened his aged eyes and smiled at her.

And so she grew through the good summer months and the people in the camp gazed at her almost with awe, for she became beautiful and of a size and strength surpassing that of any other dog in camp. And when the winter came she thrust her shoulders into harness with the other young dogs, and she gave freely of her strength to men. In the winter evenings she came into the igloo, and this was permitted by Maktuk the son, for he knew the comfort his father took from the feel of her thick fur against his ancient body. Maktuk the elder gave her the name she bore, Arnuk — The Woman — for she was wife and mother to him in the last winter of his years.

174   WildLife?

Because there can be no death while there is birth, old Maktuk himself insisted that his dog be mated in the late winter days when the moon stands still and the wild dogs, the great white wolves, howl of their passion to the flickering northern lights. So it was arranged, for Arnuk bore within her the promise of a strength that would be the people's strength in years to come. And when Maktuk, the elder, felt the throb of new life in the womb of The Woman he was content. For his love for the dog was very great, and her life was his life too.

The spring hunger had already begun before Arnuk was mated, and the famine grew with the passing days. The older dogs died first, yet near the end even Arnuk's littermates lay stiff and silent in the snows. But Arnuk's strength was great, and when there was some scrap of bone, or skin, that the people could spare, she received it — for in her womb lay the hopes of many years to come.

This was the way of things when the people turned from the lonely igloo and dragging the sleds with their own failing muscles, set their faces to the west.

The ties that bind man and his dog can be of many strengths, but the ties which bound Arnuk to old Maktuk were beyond human strength to break. Arnuk went with the people, but resisting fiercely. And on the third day of the journey she gnawed through the rawhide tether and before dawn she had vanished into the swirling ground drift of the wind-swept darkness. In the morning Maktuk, the son, held the frayed tether in his hand and his face was filled with the sorrow of foreboding. Yet when he spoke to his family it was with these words.

"What must be, surely cannot be denied. The Woman has gone to my father and she will be with him when the Snow Walker comes. But my father's spirit will know of our need, and perhaps the day will dawn when he will return The Woman to us, for if she does not come the years ahead are dark."

As for Arnuk, she reached the little igloo before dawn broke that day, and when the old man opened his eyes to see if it was the Snow Walker at last, he saw the dog instead. And he smiled and laid his bony hand upon her head, and once more he slept.

The Snow Walker was late in coming, but on the seventh day he came, unseen, and when he passed from the place the bond was broken. Yet it was not broken, for Arnuk lingered with her dead for three days more and then it was the wind perhaps, that whispered the unspoken order. ''Go to the people, go!''

When she emerged from the igloo she found her world had been obliterated beneath a heavy blizzard. For a while she stood in the pale winter sun, her golden coat gleaming against the purple shadows, then she turned her face with its broad ruff and wide-spaced amber eyes, toward the west, for that way lay her path. And within her the voices of the unborn generations echoed the voice of the wind, but with a greater urgency. ''Go to the tents of men,'' they told her. ''Go!''

With her head down, and her great plume held low, she moved westward into the pathless spaces, and only once did she pause to turn and stare for a long minute at her back-trail, waiting for some final sign. There was no sign, and at length she turned away.

This was the beginning of her journey. Death had severed the bonds that held her to one man, but she was still bound fast to men. Through untold generations the fate of her kind had been one with that of men, back through the long dim sweep of time even before the Eskimos drifted west across the island chain from Asia. Arnuk was one with the people, and her need of them was as great as their need of her.

And in this hour her need was truly great, for through the long days in the igloo she had eaten nothing, and now her hunger was six-fold, for within her the new life waxed on the substance of her body. She was in a desperate hurry to renew the links with men, and so she drove herself.

She did not halt even when darkness swept the bleak plains

into obscurity. At midnight she came to the place where she had chewed her way free of young Maktuk's sled. She knew it was the place only by an inner sense, for the snow had levelled all signs, and had drifted in all trails. She circled amongst the hard drifts, whining miserably, for terrible doubts had begun to seize upon her. She climbed a rock ridge to test the night air for some sign that men were near. Scents came to her. The acrid odour of an arctic hare that had fled into invisibility at her approach. But there was no scent of man.

Her whines rose to a crescendo, a wild pleading in the darkness, but there was no answer except the rising moan of the wind. And at length, worn into stupor by the weight of her hunger, and by her loneliness, she curled up in the shelter of a drift and lost herself in dreams.

So the dog slept in the heart of the unfathomable wilderness. But as she dozed uneasily, a profound change was taking place in the secret places of her body. A strange alchemy was at work. She lay with her nose outstretched on her broad fore-paws and her muscles twitched with erratic impulses. Saliva flowed to her mouth, and in it was the taste of blood. In her mind's eye she laid her stride to that of the swift deer, and her teeth met in the living flesh and she knew the savage ecstasy of the last quiver in a dying prey.

From somewhere out of time the ageless instincts that lie in all living cells were being re-born, so that the dog, and the new life within her, would not perish. And when Arnuk raised her head to the dawn light, the thing was done, the change complete.

The dawn was clear, and Arnuk, her perceptions keenly sharpened by the chemistry of change, tested the wind. When she found the warm smell of living flesh, she rose to seek it out.

Not far distant, a Snowy Owl, dead white and shadowless in the pre-dawn, had earlier swept across the plains with great eyes staring. The owl had seen, and fallen so swiftly on a hare, that the beast had known nothing until the inch-long talons clutched his life and took it from him. It was a good kill, and the owl felt pleasure as it perched above the corpse. The great bird savoured the weight of its own hunger, and while it sat complacent, crouched above the hare, it did not see the flow of motion on a nearby drift.

Arnuk was a weasel creeping up upon a mouse; a snake slithering upon a sparrow. Skills she had never known, skills that had come to her in all completeness from forgotten half-beasts lost in the dimmest aeons, were hers now. Her belly dragged on the hard snows and she inched forward. When she was a dozen feet away, the owl raised its head and the yellow eyes of the bird stared with expressionless intensity full into Arnuk's face. Arnuk was the stillness of death, yet every muscle vibrated in the grip of a passion such as she had never known before. And when the owl turned back to its prey, Arnuk leapt. The owl saw the beginning of the leap and threw itself backward into its own element with a smooth thrust of mighty wings. But those wings were a fraction slow and the hurtling form of the dog, leaping six feet into the air, struck flesh beneath the feathers.

It was a brief battle. Three times the talons of the bird drew blood, and then they stiffened and relaxed in death.

Arnuk slept afterwards while white feathers blew into the bleak distance, and tufts of white fur moved like furtive living things in the grip of the wind. And when she woke again the agony of her hunger was at an end and the savage drive of her new instincts was momentarily dulled. Once more she was man's beast and lost.

She woke, and without a glance at the red snow beside her, set out again into the west, unconscious, yet directly driven.

The people whom she sought were wanderers on the face of a plain so vast that it seems limitless. The dog could not conceive of the odds against her finding them, but in her memory was the image of the summer camp where she had spent her youth, and with an unerring perseverance she set her course for that far distant place.

A day and a night, and nearly a hundred miles of scarred rock ridges where the snow-demons rose and whirled like dancing spirits, separated her from the place of the owl before weariness brought her to a halt again. And in all that space she had seen no trace of men. Few were the beasts or birds that moved upon that sullen desolation and the world seemed empty of all forms of life except the dog. Yet this was an illusion, and Arnuk, sleeping fitfully in a snow-hollow, was roused to reality by the new senses that had quickened in her. She sat up abruptly and the long hair of her ruff lifted stiffly. The white dawn was breaking, but this time it brought no promise of food. Instead it brought cold fear.

Arnuk could not tell how she had been warned, and yet the warning was implicit. Her ruff was a flag of her courage, and she growled deep in her broad chest. There was nothing to be seen, or heard, or smelled — and yet she knew. Leaping from her snow bed she raced toward the long line of a gravel ridge that had been burnished clear of snow by the winter gales.

The light was breaking when she reached the high ground and there, where two huge rocks stood up like tombstones, she took her stand, facing her back trail. And at last she saw the shadows, four of them, weaving and fading in the dim light, but drawing always closer.

She knew them. Many times, while she still lived in the security of men's camps, those shadows had circled beyond the fire-light, singing their blood-stirring songs. And the dogs of men had lifted their heads and flung back the challenge with an hysterical ferocity. For the dogs of men and the dogs of the wilderness walk apart, theirs being the hatred of brothers who have denied their common blood.

Arnuk was afraid. She crouched close to the rocks and waited while the shadows flickered in the rising dawn, drew closer, and halted silently a dozen yards away.

Dimly Arnuk understood that a law had been broken, and that when she had come unannounced into the territory of the wolves she had invited death. Hatred of the 'others' welled up within her. The new forces that had come to her gave her a savage will to live. Her lips drew back and her white teeth glistened as she tensed herself for war.

It must be that miracles are not reserved for men alone, for a miracle came to pass upon that wind-swept ridge when the leader of the wolves, a gaunt and greying giant, stood and tested the dawn wind. He faced Arnuk, his grizzled muzzle wrinkling in a strange perplexity, and after one dreadful moment of poised immobility, his straining muscles eased, and, incredibly, from his massive chest there came an almost plaintive whine. The wind blew gustily and a veil of driven snow rolled up the ridge. And when it passed, the dog Arnuk was alone. The wolves had vanished utterly, swallowed by the anonymity of night, and the dog understood that she was spared. Perhaps she may have understood that there are many laws amongst the 'others' and chief of all is the one which gives immunity to a female ripe with new life, even though she be an outlander from a different world. The wolves had known, and Arnuk once more took up her journey, aware that there was peace between her and the wild ones whose land this was.

The days passed and after each the sun stood a little higher in the sky. Space lengthened under the dog's feet and the explosion of spring disturbed the world. The snows grew soft and the Barrens' rivers, freed from their chains, thundered angrily across the plains. In a white and glaring sky flights of ravens hung like eddies of burned leaves and on the opening ponds geese mingled with the raucous flocks of gulls.

The awakening of life was in the deep moss, where the lemmings tunneled, and it was on the stony ridges where cock ptarmigan swaggered before their mates. It was in all living things and in all places, and it was within the womb of the dog Arnuk. Her journey had been long, and her broad paws were crusted with the dried blood of a hundred stone-cuts. Her magnificent coat was matted now, and lustreless under the spring suns. Nevertheless she drew upon hidden strengths and upon her own indomitable will, and she went forward into the western plains.

Gaunt, hot eyed and terribly exhausted, she brought her quest to an end on a day in early June. Breasting a long ridge she saw before her the brilliant light of sun on roaring water and she recognized the River. She had come home.

Whining with excitement she ran clumsily down the slope, for her body had grown awkward in these last days. And soon she was amongst the rings of weathered boulders where, in the summer that was past, men's tents had stood.

The tents were gone. There was no living man to welcome the return of the lost one. Only on the nearby ridges the motionless piles of rocks that the Eskimos called Inukok, Men of Stone, were there to see the coming of Arnuk. They, and the hidden piles of bones under rock cairns near the river, the old graves of forgotten people. Arnuk understood that the place was empty of living men, yet for an hour she refused to believe it. Pathetically she ran from old tent-ring to old meat-cache, sniffing each with a despairing hope, and finding nothing to give her hope, and when realization became inescapable, the dog curled herself in a depression beside the place where old Maktuk had once held her at his knees, and she gave herself up to her great weariness and to her bitter disappointment.

Yet the old camp was not as empty as it looked. While Arnuk made her fruitless search she had been too preoccupied to know that she was being watched. Had she glanced up the river to a low cliff she might have seen a lithe shape that followed her every move with eyes that held in them a hunger not born in the belly. She would have seen and recognized the wolf, and her hackles would have risen and her teeth been bared.

The wolf was almost as young as the dog. Born the preceding spring he had stayed with his family for a full season until in the early spring of this year, the urge to wander had come over him and he had forsaken his ancestral territory. Many adventures had befallen him, and most had been bitter ones for he had learned, at the cost of torn flanks, and bleeding shoulders, that each wolf family guards its own land and there is no room for a stranger. His tentative offers of friendship had been met with bared teeth in the lands of three wolf clans before at last he came to the River and found a place where no wolves were.

It was a good place. Not far from the empty Eskimo camp the River flared angrily over a shallow stretch of rounded boulders to lose itself in the beginning of an immense lake, and at the shallow place the caribou had made a ford in their spring and summer migrations. They crossed the river here in untold thousands, and not all escaped the river's anger. The drowned bodies of dead deer lay amongst the rocks at the river mouth, and there was ample food for a great population of arctic foxes, ravens, and white gulls. But the wolves of the area did not visit the place for it belonged to man, and that which man claims to himself is forbidden to the great wild dogs.

Knowing nothing of this prohibition the young male wolf had taken up his home by the river, and here he nursed his loneliness. Perhaps even more than dogs, wolves are social beasts, and the 'lone wolf' is only a legend. Companionship in the hunt, and in the games that are played after the hunt, are vital to the happiness of the great white beasts. Isolation from their own kind is purgatory for them, and they can know a loneliness that eats away the heart.

It had been so with the young wolf, and when he saw and smelled the dog Arnuk, he was filled with conflicting emotions. He had seen no dog before, yet he sensed that the golden coated beast below him was not quite of his blood. The smell was strange, and yet it was familiar. The shape and colour were strange, and yet they roused in him a warmth of memory and desire.

He had been rebuffed so many times before that he was cautious now, and when Arnuk woke from her sleep of exhaustion she did not at first see the stranger, but her nostrils

182   WildLife?

told her at once of the nearness of deer meat. Her hunger was savage and overpowering. Without caution she leapt to her feet and flung herself upon a ragged haunch of caribou that had been dragged to within a few yards of her. Only when she had satisfied her first desperate hunger did she glance up and meet the still gaze of the young wolf.

The wolf sat motionless a hundred feet from the dog, nor did he so much as twitch an ear as Arnuk's hackles lifted and the threat took form deep in her throat. He remained sitting, yet tense to spring away, and after a long minute Arnuk again dropped her head to the meat, satisfied that the wolf meant her no harm.

This was the way of their first meeting, the wolf and the dog. And this was what came of it.

With the mockery of this second deserted camp before her, Arnuk gave up her search for men. She could no longer fight against the insistant demands of her heavy body, and there was no more time for searching. Now once again, in her hour of despair, the hidden force within her took command. Before that first day was out her mood had changed magically from deep dejection to a businesslike alertness.

Ignoring the young wolf, who still kept his distance, Arnuk made a quick tour of the familiar ground beside the river. She carefully examined the carcasses of five drowned deer, and from each of these she chased the screaming gulls and guttural ravens, for this meat was hers now by right of greater strength. Then, satisfied with the abundant food supply, Arnuk left the river and trotted briskly inland half a mile to where a rock outcrop had opened its flanks to form a shallow cave. Here, as a pup, Arnuk had played with the other dogs of the camp. Now, as a full grown female, she examined the cave with more serious intent. The place was dry, and protected from the winds. There was only one thing wrong, and that was the smell of the cave. It was pervaded by a potent and unpleasant stench that caused Arnuk to draw back her lips in anger and distaste — for no animal upon the face of the great plains has any love for the squat and ugly wolverine. And a wolverine had clearly used the cave during the winter months.

Arnuk's nose told her that the wolverine had been gone for several weeks and there was little likelihood that he would return until the winter winds forced him to seek shelter. Arnuk scratched earth and sand over the unclean floor, then set about dragging moss into the deepest recess. And here at last she hid herself and made surrender to her hour.

Arnuk's pups were born on the third day she spent in the cave, on a morning when the cries of the white geese were loud in the spring air. It was the time of birth, and the five squirming things that lay warm against the dog's fur were not alone in their first day of life. On the sand ridges beyond the river a female ground squirrel suckled the naked motes of flesh that were hers, and in a den by a ridge a mile distant an arctic fox, already greying into summer coat, thrust his alert face above the ground while the feeble whimpers of the pups his mate was nursing warned him of the tasks ahead. All living things in the land by the river moved to the rhythm of the demands of life new born, or soon to be born. All things moved to this rhythm except the outcast wolf.

For the three days that Arnuk remained hidden, the young wolf felt a torment that gave him no peace. Restless and yearning for things he had never known, he haunted the vicinity of the cave. He did not dare go too close, but each day he dragged a piece of deer meat within a few yards of the cave mouth, and then drew back to wait with pathetic patience for his gift to be accepted.

On the third day, as he lay near the cave snapping at the flies which hung about his head, his keen ears felt the faintest tremors of a new sound. He was on his feet instantly, head outthrust and his body trembling with attention. It came again, so faint that it was felt rather than heard — a tiny whimper that called to him across the ages and across all barriers. And in that instant his loneliness was done. His great unease was at an end.

184 WildLife?

He shook himself sharply, and with one quick, proprietary glance at the cave mouth, trotted out across the plain — no longer a solitary outcast, but a male beginning the evening hunt that would feed his mate and pups. So, simply and out of his deep need, the young wolf filled the void that had surrounded him through the torturing weeks of spring.

Arnuk did not easily accept the wolf in the role he had chosen to play. For several days she kept him at bay with bared teeth, although she ate the food offering he left at the cave mouth. But before a week was out she had come to expect the fresh meat; the tender ground squirrels, the arctic hares, and plump ptarmigan. And from this it was not really a long step to total acceptance of the wolf who, by his every action and by his whole demeanour, expressed his self-imposed devotion to his adopted family.

The neighbour fox, a grey shadow on the rocks above the cave, was the only watcher on the morning when Arnuk sealed the compact with the wolf. The little fox watched with his usual curiosity as the big dog paused by the carcass of a fresh-killed hare, then glancing past it saw the sleeping form of the young wolf. The fox watched as the dog stepped forward one slow pace at a time until she was standing close to the exhausted hunter. And the fox watched as the husky's brush wagged slowly, as the wolf raised his head, and as the two great beasts touched noses.

In the days that followed, the fox saw much of the happenings at the cave, for he was a fearless little beast, and he knew that the wolf regarded him with disinterested neutrality. Coming back to his own kits after a mouse hunt, he would sometimes detour to pass close to the cave and then he would pause and bark sharply at the sight of the five golden pups that flung themselves over the inert body of the wolf, snapping at his tail and ears, and scratching sand into his half closed eyes.

Often the fox followed the wolf on the long night hunts — but at a discreet distance, for this was business and it was unsafe to come too close to the great hunter. They were long hunts, for the wolf had marked out for his adopted family a territory of nearly a hundred square miles, and each night he circled his domain harvesting the food that was now his by right.

As for Arnuk, her life was without complaint. There were no fears to bother her, and there were no empty spaces in her heart. As the pups grew larger she weaned them, and then for a few hours each day she was free to enjoy the somnolent pleasure of a sunny hour lying still as death beside a lemming's run, waiting for the sweet morsel of flesh that might be her reward for patience.

Occasionally she visited the empty camp of men, but she no longer felt the old longing tugging at her. Her life was full.

So the days passed until the pups were in their seventh week. Mid-summer in the Barrens, and the herds of deer were drifting southward once again. The crossing place was once more thronged with caribou, and the young calves grunted beside their ragged mothers while the old bucks, their velvet covered antlers reaching to the skies, followed aloofly in the van.

And then one evening a desire for the long chase came over Arnuk, and in the secret ways that men know nothing of, she made her restlessness and her desire apparent to the wolf. When the late summer dusk fell, Arnuk went out alone into the darkening plains, secure in the knowledge that the wolf would stay behind to guard the pups until her return.

She did not intend a long absence, only a few hours at the most, but near the outskirts of the territory she came on a band of young buck deer. They were fine beasts, and fat, which at this time of year was a mouth-watering oddity. Tired of too much lean meat, Arnuk knew a sudden surge of appetite and she circled the resting herd, filled with an ardent hunger.

An eddy of the uncertain breeze betrayed her, and the startled deer sprang to their feet and fled. Arnuk was hungry, and the night was a hunter's night. She took up the long chase.

So the hours drove the brief night from the land and when the hard early winds of dawn rose in the north the young wolf roused himself from his vigil by the cave-mouth. A sense of dim foreboding made him turn to the den and thrust his head and shoulders into the entrance. All was well, and the pups were rolled together in a compact ball, whimpering and jerking their stubby legs in sleep. Yet the feeling of uneasiness persisted in the wolf's mind and he turned toward the river where the grey light picked out the long roll of distant ridges.

Perhaps he was worried by the long absence of the dog, perhaps he had been warned by senses that remain unknown to us. His uneasiness grew and at last he trotted away from the den following the cold trail of Arnuk, hoping to see her golden form approaching from inland.

He had gone no more than a mile when the vague sense of something evil took concrete form. A vagrant eddy brought the north breeze to his nostrils and instantly he knew what had disturbed him when he woke. He turned back toward the cave with startling speed and broke into a hard gallop.

As he breasted the slope beside the den, the stink of wolverine rose like a foul miasma in his nostrils and the young wolf was transformed in the instant into a savage thing, distrait with the most elemental rage. He came down the slope in half a dozen gigantic leaps, his ears flat to his skull and his great throat rumbling with incoherent hate.

The wolverine, old and wise from a long life of slaughter, had winded the young pups in his old winter lair from a great distance off. He had not known any desire to revisit the foul winter den as he made his way slowly up-river, but the smell of the pups tempted him. Perhaps he would have ignored the temptation, for though he feared no living thing, he had no particular desire to meet the fury of a female wolf defending her young. But the night had been empty for him, and his cavernous belly rumbled with hunger. His temper, always vile, was edged by hunger and so in the grey dawn-light he turned from the river and circled cautiously upwind until he found a rock out-thrust that gave him cover, and from which he could observe the den. Here he waited with a terrible patience until he saw the young wolf trot from the den mouth toward the inland plains.

Still cautiously, the wolverine left his cover and slowly moved in upon the den, pausing for long moments to reassure himself that the pups were undefended. His squat, massive body hugged the rough ground as he drew closer, and now fully certain of success, he could already taste the pleasure of the killing, and the salt warmth of blood.

There was blood enough for him to taste that dawn. But it was not to be the blood of Arnuk's pups.

The young wolf's savage rush was so swift that the wolverine had only sufficient time to slew about and take the weight of the attack upon his side. It was enough to save him for the wolf's white teeth sank through the tough skin, but missed their promised hold upon the throat, and met in the sinews of the killer's shoulder. On any other beast it would have been a good hold, leading to victory, but on the wolverine it was not good enough. The wolverine knows neither fear nor pain, and its squat body is possessed of a strength equal to any beast three times its size. A weasel by blood with all the weasel's capacity for fury, the wolverine has the body of a bear, and such is its vitality, that life remains in it until that body has been literally torn apart.

So it was with the old beast at the cave mouth. He did not feel his injury, but instead was aflame with an insane anger. He swung his fifty pounds of bone and gristle into a savage counter-thrust.

Had the wolf been older, and more experienced, he might have side-stepped that lunge, but he was young, and blinded by the allegiance that he had freely given to the pups that he had never sired. He held his grip and did not slacken it as the wolverine's teeth raked his unprotected flank.

They fought in silence. The sun, red on the eastern rim, was pallid beside the glare of blood upon the rocks. The fox watched the terrible duel for an instant from its distant den, and then, appalled by the fury of that struggle, slunk into the dark earth and lay beside his mate and kits, in trembling fear. . . .

It was the gulls that warned Arnuk. From afar off as she came wearily homeward in the warmth of the morning she saw them circling, and heard their strident screams. They eddied above the rocks where the den lay, and weary as she was she mustered her strength and came on at full pace. And so she found them, the murderer torn to bloody fragments before the murder was begun. And so she found the wolf, his throat ripped raggedly across, and his still body stiffening beneath the rising sun.

The bodies still lay near the cave when, a week later, the voices of men echoed once more along the shores of the river. And they still lay by the cave a little later on when the young man called Maktuk bent down to the dark opening and very gently thrust his hand under the frightened pups, while Arnuk, half wild with old emotions, stood trembling by his side. Maktuk was a man of the great plains and he could read much that cannot be written, so that he knew all there was to know of what had taken place beneath the ragged rocks.

And it was because he knew, that on an evening in late summer he took his son to the bank of the river, and placed the boy's hand on the head of the golden dog, and spoke these words.

"Maktuk, my son. In a little time you shall be a man and a fine hunter, and all the wide plains will know your name and skill. And in those days to come you will have certain friends to help you in the hunt, and of these, the greatest you shall always call *Arnuk,* and then my father will know that we have received his gift, and he will be at ease. And in those times to come all beasts shall fall to your spear and bow — save one alone. For never shall you lift your hand against the white one, against *Amarok* the great white wolf — and so shall our debt be paid."

The Wolf

E. Pauline Johnson

Like a grey shadow lurking in the light,
He ventures forth along the edge of night;
With silent foot he scouts the coulee's rim
And scents the carrion awaiting him.
His savage eyeballs lurid with a flare
Seen but in unfed beasts which leave their lair
To wrangle with their fellows for a meal
Of bones ill-covered. Sets he forth to steal,
To search and snarl and forage hungrily;
A worthless prairie vagabond is he.
Luckless the settler's heifer which astray
Falls to his fangs and violence a prey;
Useless her blatant calling when his teeth
Are fast upon her quivering flank — beneath
His fell voracity she falls and dies
With inarticulate and piteous cries,
Unheard, unheeded in the barren waste,
To be devoured with savage greed and haste.
Up the horizon once again he prowls
And far across its desolation howls;
Sneaking and satisfied his lair he gains
And leaves her bones to bleach upon the plains.

It Began

Jon Whyte

with an involvement of certain grey wolves
        in a green wood,
and went on to a circle inscribed
        in wind-hardened snow.

It begins again
with an involvement of green eyes
            and yellow teeth
and goes on to a spiral tightening
            upon an elk.

It ends
with a blood-spattered, grass-ragged patch
            and a carcass
and snow whorls covering the spot
            in a levelling wind.

It began again
with an involvement of grey wolves
            in a dark green wood.

The Hunters of the Deer
Dale Zieroth

The ten men will dress in white
to match the snow and leave the last
farmhouse and the last woman, going
north into the country of the deer. It
is from there, and from past there, that
the wind begins that can shake
every window in the house and leaves
the woman wishing she had moved away
five years and five children ago.

During the day the father of her children
will kill from a distance. With the others
he will track and drive each bush
and at least once he will kill before
they stop and come together for
coffee in scratched quart jars. And
sometimes the November sun will glint
on the rifles propped together in the snow.

In the evening, as they skin and gut,
they talk about the one that ran three
miles on a broken leg and the bitch wolf
they should have shot and how John
the bachelor likes eating more than
hunting and they pass the whiskey
around to keep warm. In the house
the woman makes a meal from pork.

These men are hunters and later,
standing in bright electrically lighted
rooms they are sometimes embarrassed with the
blood on their clothes and although the
woman nods and seems to understand,
she grows restless with their talk.
She has not heard another woman in fourteen days.

And when they leave, the man sleeps
and his children sleep while the woman
waits and listens for the howling of
wolves. And to the north, the grey
she-wolf smells the red snow and howls.
She also is a hunter of the deer.
Tonight, while other hunters sleep, she
drinks at the throat.

Deathlocks

Andrew Suknaski

for sid marty

winter moves down
from the mountains —
last night frost flamed
the larches into orange

this morning
on the trail into boom lake
cold wind curves my scent
into nostrils of two bull elk
facing one another
in a meadow

the elk briefly glance
my way
& then begin to spar —
i listen to faint clicking sounds
of antlers
till the elk cease
their playful sparring
(it will grow more serious
in a week or two)

as the elk graze a while
& then face one another
something brings to mind pale images
of two farmers i saw fight once
at a dance in a prairie school
(i remember the look of melancholy
in their eyes
before the frost of hate
flamed their faces red —
the sound of cracking bones
as their fierce arms locked
while a young girl cried
in the forest of people
surrounding them)

Wild Horses
Myra A. I. Smith

We saw them drink from a quiet stream,
    As clear as their own dark eyes;
Their necks were arched in the sunlight's gleam
And they were beautiful as a dream
When they drank at dawn from a quiet stream,
    As clear as their own dark eyes.

We saw them run on the open plains,
    Untouched by the whip and spur;
The wind was soft in their tossing manes,
The love of freedom was in their veins,
As they ran for joy on the open plains,
    Untouched by the whip and spur.

We saw them stand on a hilltop high
    With nostrils wide to the breeze.
Their forms were graceful against the sky,
And wild and beautiful was their cry
As they stood at eve on a hilltop high
    With nostrils wide to the breeze.

On Highway 16, Jasper
Sid Marty

Leaving the swamp at night
the moose was a dark cloud
floating in mist, to cross the road

Lights stopped him, hypnotized
and the first car caught him hard
in his creaking back legs

Half thrown, half lunging
fell in a spray of glass
his hocks torn open
an animal never pushed that hard before
got up and fell into the ditch
to the water there, safe element

Trailing one shattered leg
learning all in a moment
in acceptance, how obvious
the death dealing highway is

as the trail of a wolverine, a stink
that deer avoid
the look and smell of it
signifying death

Moosewa swam to a willow thicket
catching his useless leg on a snag
he found the dark centre of pain
and trembled

Next day drove him further in
struggling wild as the deer flies
clumped on his wounds and fed

the sun a swollen burr in his skull
whose brittle pricks jarred each nerve,
the red sky eclipses
to a black moon

The Black Stallion and the Red Mare
Gladys Francis Lewis

The Outlaw Band

At first Donald lay still. Scarcely a muscle moved. The boulders and the low shrubs screened him from view. Excitement held him motionless. His hands gripped the short grass and his toes dug into the dry earth. Cautiously he raised himself on his elbows and gazed at the scene below him.

There in his father's unfenced hay flats was the outlaw band of wild horses. They were grazing quietly on the rich grass. Some drank from the small hillside stream. Donald tried to count them, but they suddenly began moving about and he could not get beyond twenty. He thought there might be two hundred.

Donald knew a good deal about that band of horses, but never had he had the good luck to see them. They had roamed at will over the prairies, trampling down the grainfields and leading away many a domestic horse to the wild life. Once in that band, a horse was lost to the farm. They were known over many hundreds of square miles.

There in the flats was the great black stallion, the hero or the villain of a hundred tales. Over the far-flung Saskatchewan plains and grass lands there was scarcely a boy who had not thrilled to those tales. There was scarcely a boy who had not dreamed of wild rides, with the great body of the stallion beneath him, bearing him clean through the air with the sharp speed of lightning.

There was the stallion now, moving about among the horses with the confidence of a king. As he moved about, teasingly kicking here and nipping there, a restlessness, as if they sensed danger, stirred through the band. The stallion cut to the outside of the group. At a full gallop he snaked around the wide circle, roughly bunching the mares and colts into the smaller circle of an invisible corral.

He was a magnificent creature, huge and proudly built. Donald saw the gloss of the black coat and the great curving muscle of the strong legs, the massive hoofs, the powerful arch of the neck, the proud crest of the head. Donald imagined he could see the flash of black intelligent eyes. Surely a nobler creature never roamed the plains!

Off wind from the herd, a red mare came out from a fold of low hills opposite. She stood motionless a moment, her graceful head held high. Then she nickered. The black stallion drew up short in his herding, nickered eagerly, then bolted off in the direction of the mare. She stood waiting until he had almost reached her, then they galloped back to the herd together.

The shadows crept across the hay flats and evening stillness settled down. A bird sang sleepily on one note.

Donald stirred suddenly. He must tell his father and help to send news around the countryside. He was still greatly excited as he crept back from the brow of the hill and hurried home. All the time his mind was busy and his heart seemed bursting.

Three hundred years ago stout-hearted Cortez and his Spaniards had brought the first horses to Mexico. Descendants of these horses had broken away and wandered into the Great Plains. The horses that Donald had watched were of that strain — Spanish, with the proud blood of Arabia in them. Thousands of them spread through the ranch country of the United States, and even north of the Canadian border. This band now grazed wild over the parklands of Saskatchewan, two hundred and fifty miles north of the Montana boundary.

Donald knew that his father, like every other farmer for miles around, was determined to round up the horses and make an end of the wandering. The outlaws had caused enough damage. Besides, when broken to saddle and harness, they would be worth many dollars, and money was none too plentiful among the homesteaders.

As a farmer's son, Donald knew that this was necessary and right. But a certain respect for the band, and the fierce love that

The Black Stallion and the Red Mare 197

he felt toward all wild free creatures, made him wish in his heart that they might never be caught, never broken and tamed. He, who was so full of sympathy for the horses, must be a traitor to them!

When he stood before his father half an hour later, he did not blurt out his news. It was too important for that. But his voice and his eyes were tense with excitement. "That band of wild horses is in the hay hollow west of the homestead quarter," he said. "There must be close to two hundred."

His father was aware of the boy's deep excitement. At Donald's first words he stopped his milking, his hands resting on the rim of the pail as he looked up.

"Good lad, Donald!" he said quietly enough. "Get your supper and we'll ride to Smith's and Duncan's to start the word around. Tell Mother to pack lunches for tomorrow. We'll start at sun-up." He turned to his milking again.

The Round-up

Smith and Duncan and the other homesteaders were in the yard shortly after daybreak. Donald afterward wondered how long it would have taken real cowboys to round up the band of wild horses. His father and neighbours were farmers, not ranchers. They knew horses; but not how to round them up in large numbers. During the next two weeks they were to learn a great many tricks of the rancher's trade.

Twenty men started out after the band as it thundered out of the hay flats, through the hills and over the country. The dust rose in clouds as their pounding hoofs dug into the dry earth. The herd sped before the pursuers with the speed of the wind. The black stallion led or drove his band, and kept them well together. That first day the men caught only the young colts.

At sunset the riders unsaddled and staked their horses by a poplar thicket, ate their dry lunches and lay down to sleep under the stars. The horses cropped the short grass and drank from the stream. Some slept standing, others lay down. At dawn the herd was spied moving westward. With the coming of night, they too had rested. For a mile or more they now sped along the rim of a knoll, swift as broncos pulled in off the range after a winter out. The black stallion was a hundred feet ahead, running with a tireless easy swing, his mane and tail flowing and his body stretched level as it cut through the morning mists. Close at his side, but half a length behind him, ran the red mare. The band streamed after.

After that first day's chase and the night under the stars, Donald had ridden back home. Not that he had wanted to go back. He would have given everything that he owned to have gone on with the men. But there were horses and cattle and chores to attend to at home, and there was school.

The round-up continued. Each day saw the capture of more and more horses. As the men doubled back on their course, they began to see that the wild horses travelled in a great circle, coming back again and again over the same ground, stopping at the same watering holes and feeding in the same rich grass flats. Once this course became clear, fresh riders and mounts in relays were posted along the way, while others drove on from behind. In this way the wild band was given little chance for rest and feeding but had always to press on. The strain of the chase took away their desire for food, but a burning thirst possessed them, and the black stallion would never let them drink their fill before he drove them on. Fatigue grew on them.

As the round-up continued, the whole countryside stirred with excitement. At every elevator down along the railroad, the latest events of the chase were talked of. On the farms the hay went unmown or unraked, and the ploughs rested still in the last furrow of the summerfallow. At school the children played round-up at recess. Donald, at his desk, saw the printed pages but his mind was miles away, running with the wild horses, now almost exhausted.

Near the end of the second week of the chase, Donald's

father rode into the yard. Donald dropped the wood he was carrying to the house, and ran to meet his father.

"Dad, have you got the black stallion and the red mare yet?" Donald could scarcely wait for his father's slow reply.

"No, Donald lad," he said, "though those two are the only horses still free. They're back in the flats. We'll get them tomorrow."

Donald felt both relief and fear.

In the yellow lamplight of the supper table his father told of the long days of riding, of the farms where they had eaten and rested, and of the adventures of each day.

"That was a gallant band, lad!" he said. "Never shall we see their equal! Those two that are left are a pair of great horses. Most wild horses come to have no wind and no muscle. But these are sound of wind and their muscles are like steel. Besides that, they have intelligence. They would have been taken long ago but for that."

No one spoke. Donald felt that his father was on his side, the side of the horses. After a long pause Mr. Turner continued.

"With his brains and his strength, that stallion could have got away in the very beginning. He could have got away a dozen times and been free now south of the border. But that was his band. He stayed by them, and he tried to get them to safety. This week when his band had been rounded up, he stuck by the red mare. She is swift, but she can't match his speed. It's curious the way they keep together! He stops and nickers. She nickers in reply and comes close to him, her nose touching his flank. They stand a moment. Then they are away again, she running beside him but not quite neck to neck. Day after day it is the same. They are no ordinary horse-flesh, those two, lad!"

There was a lump in Donald's throat. He knew what his father meant. Those horses seemed to stand for something bigger and greater than himself. There were other things that made him feel the same — the first full-throated song of the meadow-lark in the spring; ripe golden fields of wheat with the breeze rippling it in waves; the sun setting over the rim of the world in a blaze of rose and gold; the sun rising again in the quiet east; the smile in the blue depths of his mother's eyes; the still whiteness of the snow-bound plains; the story of Columbus dauntlessly sailing off into unknown seas — and now, the stallion and the mare.

These things were part of a hidden exciting world. He belonged to these things in some strange way. He caught only glimpses of that hidden world, but those glimpses were tantalizing. Something deep within him leaped up in joy.

That night Donald dreamed of horses nickering to him, but when he tried to find them they were no longer there. Then he dreamed that he was riding the great black stallion, riding over a far-flung range, riding along a hilltop road with the world spread below him on every side. He felt the powerful body of the horse beneath him. He felt the smooth curves of the mighty muscles. Horse and rider seemed as one.

Capture

A cold dawn shattered his glorious dream ride. With his father he joined the other riders. From the crest of the slope from which Donald had first seen them, the horses were sighted. They were black moving shadows in the gray mists of the early morning.

They had just finished drinking deep from the stream. Not for two weeks had the men seen the horses drink like that. Thirsty as they were, they had taken but one drink at each water hole. This last morning they were jaded and spent, and had thrown caution to the winds.

At the first suspicion of danger, they stood still, heads and tails erect, then they dashed toward the protecting hills. There the way forked.

Then Donald saw what his father had told him about. At the fork, the stallion halted and nickered. The mare answered and came close. She touched his flank with her head. Then they bounded off and disappeared in the fold that led north-west to the rougher country where the chase had not led before.

Along the way the horses had been expected to take, grainfed horses had been stationed. These had now to move over north-west. But the men were in no hurry to-day. They were sure of the take before nightfall.

The sun was low in the west when two riders spurred their mounts for the close-in. The stallion and the mare were not a hundred yards ahead. They were dead spent. Their glossy coats were flecked with dark foam. Fatigue showed in every line of their bodies. The stallion called to the mare. He heard her answer behind him. He slowed down, turning wildly in every direction. She came up to him, her head drooped on his flank and rested there. In a last wild defiance, the stallion tossed his magnificent head and drew strength for the last dash. Too late!

The smooth coils of a rope tightened around his feet. He was down. Down and helpless. He saw the mare fall as another rope slipped over her body and drew tight round her legs. It maddened him. He struggled wildly to be free. The taut rope held. The stallion was conquered. In that last struggle something went out of him. Broken was his body and broken was his spirit. Never again would he roam the plains, proud and free and monarch of his herd.

Donald saw it all. He felt it all. His hands gripped the pommel of the saddle and his knees pressed hard against his pony's sides. Tears blinded his eyes and from his throat came the sound of a single sob. It was as if he himself were being broken and tied.

The sun dipped below the rim of the plains. The day was gone; the chase was ended. The men stood about smoking and talking in groups of twos and threes, examining the two roped horses. Donald's father knelt close to the mare, watching her closely. Donald watched him. His father remained quiet a moment, one knee still resting on the ground, in his hand his

202 WildLife?

unsmoked pipe. Donald waited for his father to speak. At last the words came. "Boys," he said, without looking up, and with measured words, "Do you know — this mare is blind — stone blind."

A week later, Donald and his father stood watching those two horses in the Turner corral. They were not the same spirited creatures but they were still magnificent horses.

"I figured," his father said, turning to the lad, "that they had won the right to stay together. I've brought them home for you, Donald. They are yours, lad. I know you will be good to them."

Barra Lad's Fabulous Leap
Marg Gilkes

The little bay foaled at the B.C. Provincial Mental Hospital's Colony Farm at Essondale in 1918 was an unplanned addition to the farm's prize stable. A French coach mare had got into the corral with Craigmore Peer, a champion Hackney stallion, and conceived the creature that would thrill a continent with his ability as a high jumper.

A thin white strip down his face broadened and changed color to cover his whole nose in a pinkish tint. Chunky of build, with wideset, intelligent eyes, he was as friendly as a puppy and as playful as the sea breeze. He never went around anything; he always jumped joyfully over it.

Billy McVeigh, the farm superintendent, liked the little fellow and spent long hours schooling him on the end of a rope and teaching him to lie down to be mounted. But his habit of sailing over fences for the sheer love of it made him hard to control, and in the spring of 1921 McVeigh reluctantly decided to sell him. He was sold to Peter Welsh of Calgary, a Scots-born horse trader whose passion was high jumpers.

Shrewd and whipcord-tough, Welsh had put together a string of the best timber-toppers in the country.

He had taught six of his seven children to ride — by putting them on horseback and making them get back on every time they fell off. Each in turn became a fine rider, thrilling crowds at the best horse shows of the day, and the Welsh home came to look like a trophy shop. But for Peter Welsh the greatest achievement would be to own the world's champion high jumper.

He renamed his new horse Barra Lad, after his wife's home in Scotland, and stabled him with Mademoiselle, an 18-year-old grey mare, one of the sweetest hunter-style jumpers in North America. An amazing friendship sprang up. It was as if the orphan colt had found a mother. He hated to be apart from her and she doted on him. At night they nuzzled noses in the stall, whinnying as if talking over the events of the day.

Welsh set his 13-year-old son Louis, to ride Barra Lad. The boy had some kind of magic in his hands and voice that the horse responded to with all the affection of his nature.

"He was such a clown," said Louis. "He'd gallop in one spot just to play! He was strong and wasn't scared of a man — more like a dog. He was gentle and quiet and such good company when he was away from all the jumping and all that messing around. Yet when he got in the ring he got so excited we couldn't hold him."

Welsh grew more excited every day about his new horse. He took him across the continent with his string of high jumpers and Barra Lad routed all other horses until there was no competition left. And the competition was *stiff*. Louis as a boy was riding against men and the best of horses. Jumping Barra Lad was definitely not for fun. It was something Louis was told to do and he did it. Fun was the quiet rides the boy took in the country on the friendly bay. But mostly it was business.

In 1924, Peter Welsh formed a rodeo company with a famous rider of the day, Strawberry Red Woll. To handle publicity for the rodeo, he enlisted Fred Kennedy, a Calgary *Morning Albertan* reporter. After a year, Strawberry Red withdrew from the partnership and Welsh began a new outfit called the Alberta Stampede Co., which came to be Canada's first travelling competitive rodeo. Wherever it went the high jumpers went. Barra Lad and the Welshes continued to fascinate the crowds. But everything was leading up to an attack on the world's high-jump record — 8 feet, $^{13}/_{16}$ inches — held by Great Heart, owned by the Peabodys of Chicago. Peter signed a contract with the organizers of the British Columbia Provincial Exhibition Stampede and Horse Show. The event was to be featured in New Westminster on September 12, 1925.

The day came and the attention of horse lovers all over North America was centered on the event. All day long the usual rodeo events attracted thrill seekers, but everyone was waiting to move into the arena at night. Louis wanted to try in the afternoon because he thought Barra Lad jumped better outside, but the organizers wanted to collect from another crowd.

"I did just what I was told to do," he said.

The arena was supposed to hold 5,000 people but the crowd swelled to 6,000 since tickets were still being sold. The building was old and aside from the possibility of collapse there was fear of fire. The fire marshal and the building inspector attempted to stop ticket sales and even tried to put people out who had already paid.

While this was going on, Barra Lad took the six-foot jump, then the seven-foot. He had come into the arena strangely quiet — Louis thought at the time that it was because he was the only horse there — but with the commotion and the excitement the horse began to get keyed up. Sixteen-year-old Louis was anxious to get it over with.

Two jurists officiated at the measuring. It was a "held poles" competition. With Josie Welsh on one side and Fred Kennedy on the other, the idea was to release the top bars if it looked like either the rider or the horse was in trouble. When Kennedy stepped out with his megaphone and announced the attempt at the world's high jumping record with the bar set at 8 feet $1^1/_2$ inches, you could have heard a pin drop.

All eyes were on Louis and the seven-year-old, white-faced bay. The boy carefully walked Barra Lad up to the jump and let him look at it. Gently, he was taken back, then turned and made for the jump.

"He ran down, but then suddenly, just like a quarter horse, he turned very sharply sideways," said Louis. "He just — boom — stopped on the first try." Some of the lower poles knocked loose with his rump as he stood there, not knowing what to do. Then Louis yelled, 'Hurry up and get those poles up! He's going to go!' "

A stifling silence fell on the packed arena. Six thousand people sat forward. Louis guided the horse, who seemed for the first time to be questioning the feat his master asked of him, back to the end of the ring.

The flag dropped and Barra Lad thundered toward the jump. Up he sailed. His front feet cleared the bars. His hind legs hung low. Fred and Josie were going to bring the top bars down but, with an agonizing, straining effort, the horse swung his powerful hindquarters clear. He went down onto his knees, and his head was thrust forward. But he was over. He'd jumped 8 feet $1^1/_2$ inches, and was the world champion!

The horde released its breath in a mighty shout. People jumped to their feet, laughing and weeping and applauding and slapping their neighbors on the back. They thronged around Barra Lad, fighting to touch him. A horseshoe wreath of flowers was put around his neck and the band struck up "There'll Be a Hot Time in the Old Town Tonight". The police moved in to clear a path and Louis took him to the stable to be cooled off.

That night a happy little band of horsemen talked jubilantly of a brilliant future for Barra Lad. Finally it was time to snatch a few hours sleep before pulling out early for their anticipated triumphant entry into Puyallup, Wash., where they were scheduled to perform in another horse show.

In the still hours of the morning, a phone call roused Peter Welsh from sleep. He awakened Kennedy and the others and they raced to the barn where Barra Lad, a good eater, had refused his bucket of mash. Then all of a sudden the horse had put his head down and fallen forward into the corner, bashing his head above his eyes. Blood coming from his mouth indicated internal bleeding. Two vets had got him out of the stall into the corridor where they could work on him. Dazed, Louis sat in the dirt beside his horse and gently stroked his neck as the life drained from his body.

By now the other jumpers were being led from the stable to be put on the train waiting near the barn. They stepped carefully over the dying champion on their way to the door. Mademoiselle was the last to leave. From her stall, she had been whinnying softly, growing increasingly distressed when he didn't answer. She stopped now, looked down at him and whinnied again. Barra Lad raised his head and nickered a soft good-by.

Lowering her head, she nosed him gently, then reluctantly the gray mare stepped over her beloved stablemate and was led out into the pale dawn. As the last whistle of the train carrying the other jumpers faded in the distance, the great spirit of Barra Lad slipped away.

He was buried under the green lawn beside the arena where he had jumped, and his sadly withered victory wreath was placed on his grave. An autopsy showed Barra Lad had ruptured the main artery leading to his liver. Looking back, Louis concluded the jump should never have been made. "It's too high for any horse," he said. "It's foolishness when you start jumping like that. It's crazy."

Barra Lad's spectacular leap to victory and death has not

been remembered. The arena in New Westminster burned down. No picture of this gallant horse and the daring boy who rode him hangs in any gallery or western hall of fame.

The Guinness Book of World Records credits the official Fédération Equestre Internationale high-jump record, 8 feet 1¹/₄ inches, to Huaso, ridden by Capt. A. Larraguibel Morales at Santiago, Chile, on February 5, 1949. It gives other unofficial records but makes no mention of the world record set by Barra Lad.

The Fédération Equestre Internationale, the international governing body of equestrian sport, and the American Horse Shows Association, governing body of American show jumping, were not involved with the horse shows of western Canada in 1925 when Barra Lad broke the record, and the Welshes were so distraught after the death that none of them thought of registering it anywhere. But Fred Kennedy managed to have Barra Lad's feat listed in the T. S. Andrews sports record book. His world record was officially recognized at that time by the judges present and was certainly reported in the newspapers.

If Barra Lad's great leap was indeed an official record under the prevailing rules of the day, as seems certain, then his jump of 8 feet 1¹/₂ inches, set in that hushed arena in New Westminster 53 years ago, is still the world's equestrian high-jump record.

A Message
Patricia Vickery

A message came from the Panthapars
(The Panthapars with their raggy hair)
That whoever it was caging birds within bars
Should stop immediately and be fair.
Now the Panthapars are a shaggy lot

But their eyes are quick and their tongues are quicker.
They'd just as soon blame you and shame you as not
And they don't stop to bargain or bicker or dicker.

A message came from the Panthapars
(The Panthapars with their velvet eyes)
To stop putting spiders and beetles in jars
And to stop pulling wings off butterflies.
Now the Panthapars love all living things,
Their hearts are huge and their minds are true.
They love the creature who crawls or sings
And they love the sky and the sea and you.

The Panthapars with heart and mind
Tell whoever keeps animals trapped behind bars
To stop immediately and be kind,
To follow the way of the Panthapars;
To begin to love all living things
With hearts that are huge and minds that are true,
To love the creature who crawls or sings
And to love the sky and the sea and you.

It's funny about the Panthapars
With their velvet eyes and their raggy hair
Who CARE about creatures we put inside bars —
These Panthapars live everywhere.
Their eyes are quick to see who is cruel;
And their tongues are quicker to call out "Shame!"
And they live by a wondrous and beautiful rule;
"Whoever is mean is the one to blame."

GreenSpace?

Imagine the Buffalo
C. K. Harris

imagine the buffalo   like a prairie storm riding the
tall grass   imagine   on the curled crest of hill   the
Indian pointing   and Peter Pond   his heart stayed by
the massive reef of mountains where the sky stopped

now think of the Rockies   secret lands   chill as
cathedrals and as hushed   aware of the sudden coming
expecting the clang of iron   the hum and squeal of
lifts   the whirr of choppers   and the mining

imagine those waves of rolling hills breaking against
wild mountains   glacial in white and green   mountains
hiding their sudden cracks and crevices   preparing their
cataracts and avalanches   and waiting

Description of the Cave at Banff, 1929
David Drummond Galletley

It was at one time an active geyser, spouting water and mud up
through an orifice. The springs were intermittent in their action.
They lay in repose awhile, then sprang up again, but there was
always some in place. If you had kept your eyes fixed upon the
pool you would have seen the gas and the water coming up

together. That's sulphurated hydrogen gas, the H_2S in chemistry. The whole of the cavity was at one time full of water and gas, and the gas kept the water always in a state of turmoil, tearing at the rock and converting it into mud, and when the heat got to a certain intensity, up it went through a vent sending a stream of water and mud about one hundred feet in the air. Then the cold air rushed in and filled the vacuum, and on went that grinding process as before, until it heated up the cold air. Then away it spouted again. This continued to repeat itself for thousands of years, until it made a breach in the wall, then out it rushed with a great roar, and spouted never more. It underwent an operation for appendicitis. The operation was successful but the patient died, and it has been sending forth a strong sulphurous odor ever since. That was the last of the geyser.

The temperature of the water is ninety degrees, but there is quite a stream of ordinary cold water coming from some spring in the mountain. We have never located it, but it is increasing in volume every year and it lowers the temperature to about eighty degrees. The depth of the water is about four feet. People used to bathe there until twelve years ago. Looking at the bottom of the water you could see a number of dark spots. These were holes full of quicksand and they were getting larger and larger every year. The friction of the water and the gas combined were eating, eating away the rock all the time, and enlarging the holes. Those who couldn't swim were constantly stepping into them, and getting beyond their depths, so it was considered wise to stop the bathing before any accident happened.

I bathed there about twenty-seven years ago, and there was only one hole of any consequence at that time. You can still see it situated at the opposite side. It is about the circumference of a carriage wheel. We used to have a rope stretched across from one side to the other to guard against stepping into it, for down through that hole you could thrust a pole about ten feet long and not find the bottom. All the rest of the holes that you see in front now were so small then that an ordinary Chicago foot (it's said by Bostonians that they have very large feet) might have spanned them, but now a Scottish foot can't (which are understood to be very much larger), so we stopped the bathing. We couldn't afford to have any Scots folk drowned you know, they are so very precious, and so very scarce, and yet go where you will, you will find them.

In cold weather, the steam from the cave was quite visible, and it ascended clear of the vent over twenty feet before it vanished. During cold weather, that column of steam could be seen from quite a distance. Away back in 1880, when men were surveying the CPR, the surveyors' attention was attracted to this column of steam ascending every day, and they wondered as to the cause. Guided by the steam, they came to the hole and, looking down, they saw the large cavity, but no means of ascent, no means of entrance. They reconnoitred all round to see if they could find any other opening, but there was none: the passage way at that time was full of water, a water drain. They were bound to get in, however; they were men of resources — they had an axe with them. (Place an axe in the hands of a Canadian Woodsman and he'll ''hew his way to Glory''.) They felled a couple of long trees, trimmed the branches, improvised a ladder out of these, lowered it down through the hole, and came down that way.

The sight that met their gaze must have been a glorious one. For the whole of the roof was decorated with beautiful stalactites, six, seven, eight, nine and ten feet long, and beautiful stalagmites, standing around the base, like so many sentinels at their post. In fact the whole of the interior of the cave was literally covered with beautiful crystals.

Now, wouldn't you have thought, and wouldn't you have expected also, that these men, surveyors, educated, intelligent men — they had to be to follow that vocation — stumbling accidentally, as they did, upon such a lovely cave as this, that nature had so lavishly and gorgeously adorned with crystalline beauty, that they would have been so pleased, and so proud of being the discoverers, that they would naturally have refrained from vandalism themselves, and would have protected it from others. But, alas, that was not the case. These were the men that robbed the cave of all its crystal adornment.

It would have been one of the prettiest caves on this continent, if they had left it alone — left it as they found it, and as nature made it.

The poet says "A thing of beauty is a joy forever." Well! that depends upon the thing of beauty's being in its proper place, and in this case, at any rate, the proper place of these things of beauty, these crystals, these stalactites, and stalagmites, was right where the Creator placed them, and not as they are now, kicking around the houses of Cave Robbers. They are of no intrinsic value. You can't make anything of them, they are so brittle; and they deteriorate in color from being confined. Probably they have them coffined in boxes and stowed away in some cellar, attic or outhouse. Whereas, if they had been left, what a glorious sight it would have been to the thousands and thousands of visitors who come to Banff year after year.

Now we have been deprived of that pleasure and privilege due to the selfishness, covetousness, cussedness, and wickedness of those surveyors who despoiled a beautiful "temple not made by hands" and robbed it of all its crystal adornment.

Who Wrote Upon the Rocks?
Alice A. Campbell

Near the United States border, east of Milk River in Alberta, is Writing-on-Stone Provincial Park, where grotesque rocks bear strange petroglyphs — "pictures" that were carved on the smooth side of the sandstone by a mysterious people who have vanished into the mists of time.

Not even archaeologists can find a satisfactory explanation

for the queer carvings that depict primitive buffalo hunts, horses being herded into an enclosure, two chieftains smoking the pipe of peace, and other customs still practised when the first white wanderers reached Alberta. Since James Doty — a United States Government agent sent to negotiate a treaty with the Blackfoot — first stared at "the Writings" on September 3, 1855, they have remained a riddle as intriguing as the fantastic range of sandstone rocks on which they are inscribed.

The Indians told Doty that "white men had many years ago written upon the rocks"; but Doty, like those who followed him, was satisfied that if any writings had ever been "done by the hands of white men, time has long since obliterated them". At least one missionary, the Reverend John Maclean, found that later Indians believed the writings to be the work of spirits, and therefore indecipherable. Amateur archaeologists claim they are "everything from Egyptian and Phoenician inscriptions to the prehistoric work of cave men".

We visited the park — a favourite spot for picnic parties now — on a hot summer day when haze shimmered on the horizon. Through holes in the eroded rocks, rabbits chased one another; eagles soared overhead, and shadows raced over the Sweet Grass Hills that rise loftily in Montana. Across the serpentine stream that is the Milk River, we could see the rocks and caves where American Indians hid from Custer's army. There, in the early days, buttons from American Army tunics were found in the sands around the caves. The Indians had stripped the enemy dead to provide comfort for their own wounded. Their own dead were placed on the high rock benches above the caves. With the passing of time, the bleached bones and arrowheads have fallen into the shifting sands below.

Some surfaces of the cliffs have been painted with a red pigment, similar to that from the Paint Pots of Marble Canyon. The pictographs show two distinct types of writing — possibly the art work of two distinct periods. One portrays all the figures in horizontal lines. This, supposedly, is the earlier type. The other consists of more lifelike figures, in circles. A chieftain can be easily recognized, and the men appear to be using shields.

Despite the erosion of the rocks in general, these writings are in a remarkable state of preservation. The park, scarcely larger than a section of land, was created by Order in Council on August 31, 1935. It is a well-kept and pleasant retreat — and a mysterious and lasting legacy from Alberta's prehistoric past.

Buchart Gardens
Denise Fair

At the turn of the century, Robert and Jenny Buchart came from Ontario to Victoria. Mr. Buchart was investigating limestone deposits on the Saanich peninsula. He found limestone and opened a cement mill at Tod Inlet. The Bucharts lived near the quarry, and when the limestone resources were exhausted there, the plant was moved to the other side of the inlet. All that was left was an ugly hole.

Mrs. Buchart could not stand the thought that a company would ruin the landscape and leave such results. It was her opinion that if the company made the mess its profits should help with the rebuilding. Mr. Buchart agreed. When she suggested planting a garden in and around the quarry, he openly admitted that he knew nothing about flowers; that would be Jenny's department.

Earth, seeds, and plants were brought in. Gardeners, under the direction of Mrs. Buchart, were hired. Eventually the old rock quarry began to look like a garden. Mrs. Buchart named it "Benvenuto" which means welcome in Italian. The gardens were opened so visitors could walk through them to admire the flowers and then move to the archery rings or the croquet lawn and, finally, to the tea room. Eventually these diversions were discontinued but the gardens have grown and flourished.

Robert Buchart died in 1943 and Jenny in 1950. The Gardens are now owned by their grandson, Ian Ross. He has expanded the gardens to cover twenty-five acres, all open to the public except for the ranch house which was Jenny Buchart's special retreat. Now the trees she planted as saplings in the bottom of the quarry reach over the tops of the walls of the sunken garden, a testimonial to one couple's work.

The Tree
Grey Owl

I

The age of a tree can be accurately estimated by means of the concentric rings, one for each year.

Six hundred and fifty years ago or thereabouts a squirrel picked up a jack-pine cone that he had dropped, amongst a score or so of others, from a tree-top on the neighbouring side-hill and carried it on its way for deposit in a cache of ripe, juicy cones that he had commenced, right in the centre of a pass in the Rocky Mountains. Arriving at his granary, he saw something that interested him, a little to the left, dropped the cone and went there, and forgot ever to come back.

There were probably a dozen cones lying there, and the cache, not being completed, was yet uncovered, and the cones eventually became scattered some few feet apart by the action of the wind and rain. They passed the Winter successfully, and the following year took root, and most of them sprouted up as little jack-pines. Immediately the struggle for the survival of the fittest began. Each seedling tried to outgrow his neighbour in order to reach for the sun, on the light of which their tiny lives depended. Thus they all grew rapidly in a kind of a race, rather a grim one for things so tender and infinitesimal. And some were slower than others and paid the penalty; they were soon overshadowed by their more precocious brethren, became sickly from lack of sunlight, were smothered and died. After five years there were seven or eight of them left, growing decorously apart, good healthy saplings.

On a day that Autumn a deer passed, and being on the lookout for something tasty, ate the top, and the ends of all the shoots off one of them, and by Spring the tree was only a dried stick. During the Winter, rabbits being numerous they stripped the bark off some of the rest, girdling them very neatly up as high as they could reach, so that these also died. Four or five years later a bull moose, during late Summer, used one of them as a scraping post to remove the velvet from his antlers, breaking it down, along with several others, in the process.

At the end of two decades the survivors were sizeable young trees, and all had a fighting chance to live to a ripe old age, when a porcupine happened along, barked cleanly from top to bottom all but one of them and went on his way to richer fields of exploitation of the country's timber resources. Being alone, the one that remained attracted no further attention from potential enemies and grew undisturbed for a century or so, becoming a tree of noble proportions, though in its exposed position, standing high in the mountain pass at the brink of the prairies, it tended to be heavy of trunk and wide spread of limb, rather than tall; and its topmost branches were bent around and over, trained permanently by the prevailing South-east wind from the plains, and pointed, like great dark arms in a sweeping gesture, always towards the North.

The tree withstood the terrific winds, sometimes of tornado velocity, that blew constantly upon it from the prairies, far below; drought, rain and snowstorm, and all the elements, each with its own specialized form of destructiveness, tried to kill, uproot or blast it, or break it down. None the less it flourished, nay, appeared to thrive on such treatment, either becoming extraordinarily hardy on account of the resistance it was forced to put up, or else it lived because it was, in the first place, unusually sturdy. Either way, it increased to an immense girth, and after two centuries of life its limbs, themselves as big as small trees, gnarled, twisted and overhanging, made a wide, arched canopy under whose shade many a passing beast took shelter from the hot sun of Summer-time, or refuge from the storms of Winter.

Animals of various kinds had travelled this pass from time immemorial, and it being fairly even footing for most of its width, a matter of two hundred yards or so, they had passed wherever caprice or the pursuit of food might chance to take them. But now the presence of the tree began to attract them, to influence their line of march. Not only was its shade or shelter, according to conditions, grateful, but animals, like humans, travel on well-defined routes from one prominent feature of the landscape to another; so that animal crossings are often to be found at spots such as an unusually large rock, through a particularly well-timbered gully, across an extra large beaver dam or an especially convenient fording place, and well-defined paths are worn between them. Because it was the last one of such a chain of links in the long and toilsome journey through the mountains, and it being, at the same time, the first of them on coming from the plains, the jack-pine became in time a kind of Mecca, towards which all the beasts who journey back and forth made each his intermittent pilgrimage to rest beneath it, and then refreshed, or perhaps having enjoyed in some dim, dream-like way, a kind of temporary fellowship with the lonely tree, went on his way. There was, besides, the added attraction of a luxurious mountain meadow that like a green carpet lay spread out on all sides from the tree, where there were flowers for those that liked them and berries, in season, for everybody, and a little running stream in which were mountain trout.

The game trail that was at last worn smooth and hard and well defined beside the tree, bore sometimes creatures that were notable, above the common run, and sometimes something noble. A great bull elk often led his herd in a long procession past it on the way to feeding grounds in the lower foothills. And every year when the first frosts turned the aspen leaves to bronze and gold, he took the meadow as his stamping ground, with the tree for its centre, and issued from there his ringing challenge to the world; until one Fall the herd had another leader and went by without him. A little band of wolves, rare animals at such an elevation, passed once, slant-eyed, grim and wary; they pattered up, moved restlessly about, and loping easily along as though on springs they pattered off again, to be no more seen — the corsairs of the Wild Lands.

Then there came a giant grizzly bear, who frequented the place from then on at regular and fairly frequent intervals. Huge and ponderous, yet good-natured, though swift and devastating when angered, king of the mountains he was, who gave place to no living thing in all that region. He was a silver-tip, and when he stood erect, the big horseshoe of silver hair upon his breast looked like some emblem of his royal degree. A gigantic beast, eight feet from nose to tail, four feet high at the shoulder, his claws full five inches long, he could be a terrible engine of destruction if aroused. Yet, aside from necessary kills he made when hungry, he was not at all a quarrelsome fellow, but loved quietude and peace and sitting in the sun, living greatly on roots and berries, and on fish that he caught in the trout stream that ran beside the meadow. Here he often fished, and having eaten lay beneath the tree and licked his paws and dozed, and maybe dreamed.

He had one great pastime, and that was to look long and steadily out across the vast expanse of prairie that stretched far below him on and on interminably, into infinity. Across these distant reaches there drifted from time to time in a dark flood, black bellowing masses that flowed over the rolling landscape like a moving carpet. And sometimes around the edge of these vast shifting waves of living creatures there rose clouds of dust, and there came up to the pass, faintly, the distant howling of wolves and mingled with it a wilder, shriller sound and the throbbing of drums, a rhythmic uproar that was strangely exciting to the bear as he listened. And these dark masses were the great buffalo herds, on whose outskirts there hung the gaunt, grey prairie wolves; and here whole tribes of tall, copper-coloured men gathered, and marching on foot, drove groups of buffalo into rude corrals, and shot them down with bows and arrows; for this was before the days when they had horses.

All this the bear saw and heard; and who can ever know what strange thoughts passed behind those small, sagacious eyes, or what unfulfilled longings surged through that mighty frame, as he gazed so steadily and so long out upon that, to him, undiscovered country with its far-off vistas and its unknown inhabitants. But it was not his home, and he never went there. And the great jack-pine, giant of its kind and old, even as he was, became to him a kind of milepost or a monument, and the companionship of the tree seemed to fill some want in his lonely life, and he began to feel, in his dim, uncouth way, that it lived and was, for all it seemed so quiet and never moved, a friend. And so he put his mark upon it with his teeth. And the tree, that had never been scored since the tiny cuts were made upon it by the rabbits' teeth, and was now covered by the concentric rings of four hundred years, felt a strange thrill go through all its fibres at this recognition, and knew then that it too had life. And when the bear was no longer there, the ground around its foot felt bare and empty, and when the huge brown beast returned and took its accustomed place, the soul of the tree would thrill, and a kind of a tremor pass among its branches; and the bear would lie contentedly beneath it and gaze out over the wide plains that spread for ever on into the Unknown.

This strange companionship went on for nearly half a century. And the giant silver-tip began to be old, very old for a bear. And there came a Spring when he lay longer and longer at a time beneath the tree until, during the late Summer, he never left it save on his short excursions to the berry patch and to the stream for water. For he was no longer able to capture the nimble mountain trout.

And now the leaves were turning, and the woods were painted with all the glory of Autumn; and the harsh outlines of the mountains were softened by the smoky haze of Indian Summer. And one day, just before the Falling of the Leaves, the bear lay in his old familiar place beside the tree, looking wistfully out over that mysterious, distant prairie that was, somehow, dimmer and more distant than it used to be, while he listened to the quiet humming of the wind in the branches of the pine. He had been very tired that day, but now a great peace came over him; and he gave himself over to his dreams. And the wide plains faded and were gone; and the voice of the tree became softer, fainter, farther off, and soon died quite away. And the life of the bear passed on.

But the tree knew that his soul would always be there.

And the ancient, ancient jack-pine stood guard above his bones, and waited for another hundred years. And this was the fate of the tree, that all who loved it should die, while it lived on, and waited until the last of them was gone. And so it stood, alone, a dark, looming Sentinel at the gateway to the mountains.

Later two eagles nested in its top, two great war-eagles, king and queen of all the air, who circled high above the mountains, ever upward, on and upward, floating without any effort, swinging wider, ever wider, pinions flashing in the sunlight. Every year several small eaglets appeared, and the nest in the summit of the tree, with its small, new inhabitants, became very important and a great care to the two royal birds; and the tree guarded them well, until after nearly a hundred years the nest was empty and the tree alone again. But other eagles came, and from then on there were always eagles nested there.

As the tree grew older its girth constantly increased. The mark put upon it by the bear had partly healed, but still remained a scar, and always would. Its beautiful purple-red bark grew thicker and the mighty limbs became more massive, gnarled and widespread. With age it grew more solid on its roots, and every Summer morning, when the sky was clear, the rising sun shone redly on the stout, heavily furrowed bark and warmed the tree, after the cool mountain night, so that it felt the life within it stirring. And as the early morning breeze touched its needles, they hummed a deep, varying chord of thanksgiving to the Master of Life — the Sun.

The Indians of the plains below also adored the sun; for to them the sun not only gave life, but caused it to endure, and drove away the Winter's snows and made the grass to grow, and brought the flowers to brighten the monotony of the treeless prairie. This was the belief of the Blackfoot people, who often looked up at the great jack-pine that stood so boldly outlined, so dark and magnificent of aspect, against the snow-capped background of the mountains. And they marvelled that a jack-pine should grow to such a size, as could be distinguished even at that distance. And to the band whose ancestral camp grounds lay within the sight of it, the giant evergreen, that had been standing there at the threshold of the mountains so long that none had ever heard when first it grew there, became symbolical of their race. And so it had been, since times no longer now remembered, a landmark and a sacred spot and held inviolate, as all landmarks were in old Indian days, and there was a tradition in this band that when it fell the Blackfeet would be driven from the plains into the mountains, and that if the Indians went first, then the tree too must fall. And the tree was looked up to with the greatest reverence.

Five hundred and eighty years from the time that a squirrel, in a moment of forgetfulness, had planted it, the tree for the first time gave shelter to a human being. A young man of the Blackfoot nation, who was soon to be initiated as a warrior, made a vow to go and stay beside this venerated, venerable tree five days and nights without food, in order to purge his soul of evil and have a vision, and then come down and tell his dream, which would be interpreted according to the wisdom of the magicians. And then, if he passed the tests, which were drastic, he would be made a warrior. Then, perhaps, a certain dark-eyed young woman would listen to his pleading and come to share with him his fine new teepee and share, too, the glory he was sure to earn in the coming war against a strange, pale race that was beginning to occupy the land.

So the young man went up and fasted five days and five nights at the foot of the sacred pine, who wondered why he did this, because the other creatures that came there always ate; and the tree was sorry for him and sheltered him with its wide branches, and played, quietly, soft music in its foliage for him to hear. Five days the young man sat and meditated, and looked out over the wide expanse of plains where he could see, far below, the distant encampment of his people, and his keen eyes could pick out the teepee in which the maiden that he loved awaited anxiously his return; at least he hoped she did and could not be sure, so unfathomable are the ways of a maiden with a man. And when he slept, he used for a pillow the skull of a grizzly bear that he had found there. And while he slept, the creatures of the wild that lived near by came close and watched him curiously, wondering what manner of beast he was, and what he did there; little mice with beady eyes who ran in and out of holes and sat erect and sniffed at him and sometimes ran across his feet; flying squirrels, like small, pale, flitting ghosts, in utter silence, soared and flickered from limb to limb above his head. A fox, with dainty, mincing steps, ears and nose delicately attuned to his surroundings, tripped lightly by, his tail streaming out behind him like a plume; and once a band of caribou, wraith-like in the moonlight, drifted soundlessly as phantoms through the meadow.

Now it was the custom among the Indians to seek a patron animal, that should appear in a vision during a vigil such as this young man had undertaken, who would henceforward be his crest, his ensign to be painted on his shield. But he dreamed of none of those that passed around him as he slept, but of a bear, a monstrous silver-tip that stood erect before him and made signs, and signalled to him with its forepaws, as sometimes is the fashion of a grizzly. And this was a lucky omen, and he decided then to take the bear for his patron beast, his totem; and moreover he found there, beneath the tree, two eagle feathers that had fallen from the nest in the widespread top, all ready for him to be made a warrior with. So in gratitude he made a mark upon the tree-trunk with his tomahawk, a long, narrow blaze, close beside the half-healed mark the bear had made so long ago. And he hung the bear skull on a short, dead limb, first placing in it an offering of tobacco, and carefully fastening the jaws in place with strings of spruce-root. This he did for a token, because the place had been lucky; and he thanked the tree, and spoke some friendly words to it before he left. And the tree quivered through every fibre when the Indian hung the bear's skull on the limb, and felt as though its old companion was nearer — quivered, too, at the words of kindness that the youth had spoken, the first time it had ever heard a human voice, save the distant yelling of the buffalo hunters.

And the tree knew, after more than a century of waiting, that now it had found another friend.

After his initiation the young man, now a warrior, went to the home of the dark-eyed maiden; and she was pleased that he had passed his warrior's test so bravely, as the open wounds upon his breast so plainly showed,* and commended him for keeping his vigil so honestly and not having cheated by carrying little bits of dried meat on his person, as some had been known

---

* A reference to a part of the Sun-Dance, in which the candidate was suspended on rawhide thongs skewered through loops cut into the flesh of his breast, and, throwing his weight on them, danced until the flesh tore out and released him. The entire ceremony, which was complicated, had also a religious significance.

to do. And so she could no longer resist his wooing; and when he pressed her for an answer she gave to him the one he wanted but had scarcely dared to hope for; though she had known it all along. And she gave to him her hand and promise — but shyly, in a low, soft voice and with her face demurely hidden behind her head-shawl, as is the manner of an Indian maid. And she said she would like to see the place where he had spent his days of fasting, and which he had said was so very beautiful.

And so she said goodbye to her parents, quite as though she were going away into a far country, which she was not, and they journeyed together up to the pass to spend their honeymoon, to spend the sunny days of the Moon of Berries on the pleasant, flower-strewn meadow, under the great arms of the sheltering pine. And here between them they pitched the new lodge of buffalo hides that had been waiting for this event so long. And although the climb was steep they had brought many comforts with them on travois drawn by horses, for since several generations the Indians had found wild horses on the plains, offspring of those that had been abandoned by pale-faced explorers from the South. And after the camp was made and the horses pastured the warrior brought his young wife some spotted trout from the stream, and berries from the meadow and sprays of flowers to deck the inside of their wigwam with, and fresh venison, and green, aromatic spruce fronds for a soft bed; he gathered cherry leaves and parched them a little before the fire to bring out the pleasant odour in them, and made of them a sweet-smelling pillow for her. And afterwards he made a fine blazing fire before the lodge, and put on his two black and white eagle feathers and his very best raiment, beaded, fringed and embroidered by the maid's own hands, secretly, this long time past, for this very occasion, which she had known full well would some day come to pass. And he took out from a gaily decorated bag a small, painted drum and sang songs to his sweetheart as they sat beside the fire beneath the mighty jack-pine, and with the high and sanguine hopefulness of youth, boasted in his chanting that some day he would be a chief. The maiden, now a wife, listened and was quite sure he would be a great man before very long; and being a woman, and practical, she dressed the hide of the deer he had killed for food, and smoked the meat and cooked the berries for their simple meals, and roasted trout before the open fire. And they were very happy there.

And the tree looked down with kindly sympathy upon them, and covered them with the protection of its widespread fan of limbs, and dropped light showers of pine-needles to make a carpet for them; and something like a sob came from the darkness among the branches far above. For the tree knew, like all the other creatures it had known, they could not live for very long, that it must outlive them and be alone again.

For this was the Fate of the tree, to live on and on, while all others died. And it resolved to make them happy while it could.

One night the young warrior dreamed that outside the teepee there sat a great brown bear, with an ensign of silver on his breast, and so vivid was this dream that he arose and looked out, but found no bear and went to sleep again. The next morning he feared to tell his wife about this, lest he alarm her, but as soon as she awoke she told him that she had seen, in a dream, a huge bear with a great white mark upon its breast that was curved upward like a bow and shone like silver, who sat before the teepee in the moonlight, and made gestures to her with its forepaws. So her husband said that he too had dreamed of a bear, that it must be a vision, and that he must make propitiation to the spirit of the bear at once, as it was now his totem. And this he did, placing in the skull all the last of his tobacco and fastening to it, so it hung down like a banner, his finest beaded buckskin belt.

And at that the tree trembled with happiness in all its branches, and the soul of the bear rejoiced.

From then on he used the figure of a bear for his crest, and painted it on his shield and quiver, and his wife embroidered it in beadwork on his rich ceremonial garments; and on any set of apparel that he wore there could be always seen the likeness of a bear, not in brilliant colours, but in the bear's own natural shade of brown.

After that the warrior made a pilgrimage to the place every year and slept one night beneath the jack-pine; and always he dreamed about the bear, who sat each time, in his vision, before his sleeping-place. And always the warrior left some offering or token to decorate the tree and to please the spirit of the silver-tip; and this he did once each Summer at the Time of Berries. And every year he renewed the blaze, and scraped away the accumulated gum from the scar the bear had put upon the tree, and renewed the offering of tobacco in the skull.

But one time he came attired differently to what he had ever been on any other visit. He was naked, save for a loin-cloth, a beaded belt that held a broad knife sheath, and his moccasins. His face and body were painted with strange devices in crimson, white and yellow, and on his head he wore an eagle-feather bonnet that spread wide, and stood out in a huge circle about his head. In his hand he carried a long pipe decorated with feathers and the quills of porcupines.

Full twenty years had passed since he first had visited this spot, and many times had he proved himself to be a brave and skillful warrior, and had fulfilled the confident prediction of his younger days, and had become a chief. And now he had come here, on this momentous occasion, to commune with the spirit of the tree, to ask for guidance from his patron, whom he called Brother, the grizzly bear. For the time was critical; tomorrow a great battle was to be fought with the pale people who were now coming in clamouring hordes to possess the land and drive the Indians out. On this battle might depend the fate of this band, of which he was now the chief.

Lighting his pipe he pointed the stem to the East, then the West, to the North and the South; then upwards towards the Sun, whom he worshipped, and downward to the Earth, whom he called his Mother. Lastly he blew a puff of smoke up among the pine-limbs and another into the bear-skull; and stepping back he raised his arms in a gesture of supplication, and bowed his head, so that the eagle bonnet fell wide open, spreading out around his head and shoulders like an enormous crown.

And as he stood there, he cried aloud:

"O you, great Tree, Sentinel of the Mountains.

"O you spirit of a Bear, my Brother.

"You are my patrons.

"Hear me.

"I want for myself, nothing; only this.

"Make me strong in battle.

"Help my knife and axe to fall heavily on the pale people, who would take away our homes.

"Make strong my arms to bend my bow and drive the arrows true.

"Help me to be brave on the field of battle.

"Not for myself I ask this.

"No longer do I fight for glory, but for my people, for my wife and children.

"The pale people are scattering the Indians like snowflakes before the wind.

"The Sun of the Indians is setting and the Sun of the pale ones is strong.

"Like the snowflakes of last year we will be consumed.

"Make me strong in battle.

"You are my patrons.

"Oh my Brothers,

"Hear me."

And the tree gave answers in the swaying and sighing of its foliage and whispered: "Be strong; we are with you." And the spirit of the bear breathed in the shadows: "I will be beside you; mighty am I in battle."

After he had made his offerings the Chief went down to the plain to his people; and on the way he fancied that he heard, in the darkness there behind him, a sound of shuffling, a soft, yet heavy padding as of some huge beast that followed him, and he said, "It is my Brother; it is the bear who follows." And this gave him courage so that on his way he planned confidently for the fight that would take place on the morrow.

Dashing into the council lodge he cried, "Let the war-dance commence! Make all your preparations quickly, for we will be victorious. Our medicine is very strong to-night. Let the young men paint themselves for the battle. Sound the war-drums, the rattles and the pipes of eagles' wing-bones! Shout the war-whoop! Be strong! To-morrow we will win." And cried again, "Be strong!" for that was the password that his patrons on the mountain had given him.

But when the pale soldiers came with the early morning daylight, they proved to be better armed than the Blackfoot warriors; they had heavier horses too, and were in greater numbers. With cannon* and rifle, revolver and sword they spread death in the encampment, sparing none; women were shot down with babies on their backs, one bullet being sometimes enough for two. Young girls and boys, old people and children were sabred as they ran, by the blue-coated soldiers who laughed and cursed as they dealt out death unsparingly. Hard pressed, the Indians fled up the pass and here, in the mountains, the cannons could not be brought to bear, and the heavy military horses could not climb so well as the light Indian ponies.

The Indians loosed their horses and drove them up the pass to safety, remaining to fight among the rocks on foot, picking off the soldiers one by one with arrows at close range, catching whole parties in ambuscade, and shooting them down, capturing their arms and ammunition, and turning the soldiers' own rifles against them.

*Gatling guns.

And on that mountain meadow, in which stood the mighty jack-pine, the fight was fought to a finish. The Indians rallied round their sacred tree; and now the tree was the centre of the conflict. And in the thickest of the fight the Chief felt beside him always the presence of the bear, no longer quiet and amicable, but swift and terrible and deadly, there beside him; and his arm was stronger because of it, and he felt new strength at every stroke and none could stand before him — "Like a bear" his warriors said among themselves. And the tree and the surrounding walls of rock echoed with the terrific sound of battle, and threw it back and forth from one to another, flung the fearful uproar back and forth between them, so that it seemed as if they too joined in the combat, while the eagles manoeuvred wildly and hovered screaming above the field of blood.

And high above the smoke and dust and din the pine stood calm and towering and collected, like some great general who overlooked the proceedings from an eminence, and laid the plan of battle and directed it.

And now the tide of battle turned. The Indians, their blood hot with the thought of their murdered families, fought fiercely, sparing no man; some were now using swords and cavalry pistols as well as rifles and fought man to man against the foe with desperate courage. The soldiers too were brave, but, hampered by heavy boots and other military equipment, were slower and less active than the naked, agile Indians, and were slain almost to a man.

So the prediction of the Chief came true, and he told the assembled warriors of what help the power of the Tree had been, and how the spirit of the silver-tip had fought so valiantly beside him. And so each Indian that still remained alive laid a thank-offering at the foot of the pine, their now doubly sacred Tree around which they had made their desperate stand and won. And the bear-skull was festooned with beautifully beaded belts and feathered ornaments, and painted shields, fire-bags and other valuables were laid against the Tree trunk or hung from limbs, to show the gratitude of the owners.

For it had long ago been said by the wise men of the nation, that while the Tree stood, so they too would live, and when it fell, the Blackfoot would be driven from the plains; and the tradition further said that if the Indians should be first destroyed, or move away, the Tree would fall crashing to the ground. And now in its shadow they had triumphed.

But the heart of the Tree was troubled, and the soul of the bear was sad, and both stood apprehensive and appalled, because of what the warriors would find when they went down to count their dead. A warrior expects to die; but there, amongst the torn-down teepees and smouldering remains of homes, women and children lay dead and mangled. And among them this Chief found his wife and two young sons. But the sorrow of all was so great that he said nothing of his own, and left the ruined encampment in the darkness and went up to the battle-ground, among the dead. And he stood beneath the tree in silence, there alone, his breath coming thickly in gasps of agony as he thought of the honeymoon that had been so happy, and of the gentle, dark-eyed maiden who had come so shyly, so timidly and yet so willingly to share his new teepee, here beneath the Tree; and his throat tightened at the memory — but this was weakness; with a stern, resolute gesture he saluted the bear-skull and the Tree, and thanked them for the victory — the victory! — and throwing himself face down on the carpet of pine-needles, in among the offerings and the tokens, he pillowed his face on a huge, twisted root and wept. He was no more a warrior, but just a man.

And there was no one there to see. And the limbs of the giant jack-pine bowed low about him, and the shade of the bear sat by and never moved, and tried to speak but could not, for sorrow.

And later, when the dew settled on the foliage of the pine and gathered there and dripped down, it fell like snow, quiet tear-drops down upon the man, and upon the still silent field of a battle that had been a victory, and yet was lost, on that mountain meadow, in the pass so long ago.

II

The whites, in too great a multitude to be overcome by small, isolated reverses to their arms, slaughtered the Indians without mercy. Where they could not prevail by honest war or justice, then broken treaties, economic sanctions, exile, whisky, entire destruction of the buffalo herds and ruthless suppression of tribal life, customs, religion, language and arts, eventually accomplished the desired results. The tide of people from nearly every country in the world, prolific as rabbits, domineering and land-hungry, swarmed across the continent like locusts, and overran it; and what they could not make use of or subdue, they destroyed. The smoke of devastating forest and prairie fires darkened the sun at noon-day. Immense areas became little better than a shambles, and whole reaches of the plains became almost impassable owing the stench arising from millions of slaughtered buffalo, among which young calves, robbed of their parents and useless to the hide-hunters, died by thousands of starvation.

The few Indians who survived now became outcasts in their own country, were herded on to reservations, under the supervision of Government agents who generally knew little about Indians, and were dishonest as often as not. There was bitter and useless fighting in which, to their shame be it said, numbers of ''friendly'' renegade Indians, with either a sheep-like submissiveness, a toadying subservience, or because knowing which side their bread was buttered on, according to temperament, helped the enemy against their own people; monuments have since been raised to some of these traitors, by the whites. Riff-raff of all kinds, often little better than hired assassins, engaged in the pastime of Indian-hunting with all the unnecessary brutality of those who know themselves to be in the wrong, and acted as scouts and guides to the troops, gaining thereby great historical reputations; some few of them were genuine frontiersmen, and respected by even those they fought against, but only too many were just plain killers having now a chance to indulge their natural propensities without getting hanged for it.

Both sides massacred indiscriminately, and terrible cruelties were perpetrated, on the one hand to gain, and on the other to keep, possession of the bloodstained soil. The original inhabitants of the country, both human and animal, became wary, elusive and unapproachable, and, not without some justification, frequently repaid broken faith with treachery.

In the mushroom border towns, the brothel and the jail were not unusually the principal buildings, and among the pale invaders there sprang up a race of gunmen and desperadoes who terrorized whole communities, and murdered and robbed and staged pitched battles against the forces of law and order.* Meanwhile the Indians sat by in helpless misery and watched, while the palefaces quarrelled and fought among themselves over the ownership of lands that belonged to none of them.

Civilization had come to the West, and *now* the West was wild — the great "Wild West" of romance, and song, and story was in its heyday.

And the Tree, who saw it all, made never a sign, just stood there very still, and dark, and silent.

---

*At the time of writing, these conditions have not much improved, the chief difference being that the scene of these activities has moved farther East, and the gunmen are of a lower order; some of the old time gunfighters were really brave men.

III

Many years after the historic battle, now long forgotten, an old man came up the trail that led through the flower-carpeted meadow in the mountain pass. He walked very slowly, uncertainly, like one whose strength is far ebbed and whose span of life must be very near its close. When he came to the immense jack-pine that stood alone, overlooking the vast panorama of the plains below, he sat down on one of the massive roots and gazed long and thoughtfully down upon the prairie.

He saw there the habitations of men scattered everywhere, no longer teepees, but the wooden dwelling of the white man, over a land partitioned off into squares in a chequer-board pattern of monotonous regularity. The dark moving masses that had been buffalo were no longer there, though their bones were piled in huge mounds and high, wide walls beside the railroad, so as to be conveniently loaded and shipped away as fertilizer. This the old man knew to be true, for he had seen them there.

And he sat and mused and gazed in silence, out across the vast sweep of the plains.

What once had been a game trail in days gone by had now become a road. First had come the trapper, who nosed out all the secret places of the Wilderness and discovered or made routes to all kinds of supposedly inaccessible spots; then came the reputed "explorer", who was seldom in the vanguard, in most cases following the trapper's lead, but getting the credit and often inflicting his name on portions of the scenery. Soon after came the missionary, good, self-denying and heroic, with the courage of his convictions, though perhaps, in the odd instance, at times a little misguided. There followed in quick succession the prospector, the whisky peddler, the cow-boy, the surveyor and the land agent. And none of them, except perhaps the trapper, even guessed that the trail on which they travelled had its being solely on account of the presence of the great, lone pine that over-shadowed them as they passed it by.

The transition from game path to pack-trail and then to road had been accomplished in less than twenty years. Each of the questing, acquisitive, adventurous spirits who passed by the big pine had filched as much as he could carry away of the Indian regalia and accoutrements that, for some reason unknown to them, had been left piled around it. All except the missionaries who, although they forbade further tree or sun "worship" among the savages, and frowned on the belief the aborigines held concerning the "souls" of dumb brutes, were nearly always honest, though they had been not unknown, upon occasion, to use the spiritual ascendancy they had gained over the Indians to the furtherance of the grasping tactics of the invaders. The bear-skull, by some caprice, or because it was of no value (for bears could be had for the shooting), was left to hang where it was; though the little mountain stream had long ago been denuded of its trout, and a large patch of timber that had stood upon its banks had been burnt, and in consequence the brook was nearly dry. The eagles had either been killed or had left the country long ago and their nest had been blown away piecemeal by the storms of half a hundred Winters.

After the first thin scattering of adventurers, the rank and file of Progress had marched into and over everything, and the cohorts of the civilization of the period, land-hungry, arrogant and avaricious, swept in and took possession — a miscellaneous host, to whom nothing was sacred save their own particular, personal gods, seeing nothing but the soil — "land" — or gold, hating Nature for the most part, looking on it and the institutions of the original dwellers in the region as something to be stamped out as soon as possible, to make room for the great god wheat — the god that was later, like the embarrassingly profitable touch of Midas, to choke and starve them.

For even the old man seated beneath the tree that had stood firm through all these quick and violent changes, could not, with all his accumulated experience, have foreseen the day when people would go hungry in a land where wheat accumulated faster than it could be used, and where men still kept on growing only wheat because it was the thing to do, and prated of bumper crops when the land was choked with wheat and last year's yield lay undisposed of in the bins. Nor would he ever have understood why greed and mismanagement should have changed so much of the fertile prairies into dust-choked deserts where even cactus and rattle-snakes could no longer live.

Steadily the old man looked out over this now, to him, forbidden land. He was no longer welcome there. He was an Indian.

Dressed in patched, ill-fitting trousers, a coat too small for him, a pair of nondescript, run-down shoes, and a drooping, wide-brimmed hat through a hole in the crown of which some short bristles of white hair protruded, he who once had been a Chief was now a tramp, begging his food from those who had dispossessed him and wearing the cast-off clothing that they gave him. He wore no underclothes or socks, and round his neck, by a string, was hung a cheap medallion on which was pictured a theological personage of some sect or other of the many that these new people had, and about whose authority they seemed never to be able to agree.

Yet, from far above the bigotry and strife, the sad, gentle eyes in the face depicted on the medal must surely have looked down, and wept in pity.

The old Indian's bearing was bowed and abject. Only his face retained an expression of dignity, enhanced by the keenness of his eyes; but apart from his steady, penetrating glance that must have daunted many a beholder in his younger days, his dark unmoving features were composed into a settled calm that was exceeded only by the graven immobility of the eternal mountains themselves. He fingered the tin medallion absently until, as though becoming suddenly conscious of it, he looked down at it. With a sharp tug he snapped the cord that held it and flung it from him. The trinket struck a rock with a little tinkle, a fantastically trivial sound in the sublime majesty of the surroundings. The old man rose to his feet, staggering a little, and the old eyes flashed and his face set in lines of startling ferocity as, with a gesture of contempt, he kicked aside the unspeakable shoes, tore off the cheap coat and flung away his hat. Naked to the waist, it could be seen that his brown wasted torso and withered frame must once have been of magnificent proportions, and as he stood he achieved a certain wild nobility of bearing. He passed his hand over two abrasions on the mighty trunk, one that had been a blaze and one a scar of some sort, both now nearly covered by ingrowing bark and discernible only as narrow clefts. He tottered weakly, and his hands found the bear skull, of which the binding strings had long since rotted apart and the lower jaws fallen to the ground; and leaning heavily on the skull he raised his head, white with the passage of nearly ninety years, and looking up into the heavy canopy of massed and interwoven branches that, like a deep, wide-spreading transept, arched high above him, he began to speak.

"O Tree, my patron; you and I have lived very long, each after his kind.

"Too long have we lived.

"Too long.

"The Past has fallen and lays about our feet like an old, discarded garment.

"Let it lay, lest when we pick it up it fall to pieces and be for ever lost.

"Of those who knew this great Past only you and I remain.

"Only you and I are left to remember.

"Not for long now will our hearts be obliged to carry this burden, so great a load of memories to be borne by only two.

"Our people are gone and the pale ones have taken everything.

"Now our work is done, yours and mine.

"Before your limbs are white with Winter's snows and the

240   GreenSpace?

Ghost Birds of the North whistle on white wings through the forest, I will meet her who was the mother of my sons.

"I will see the great bear whose spirit fought beside me here against the soldiers.

"Soon you will join us, for now the Indians are gone you too must go.

"The wise men of olden times, who knew you when you were young, have told it.

"It will be as they have said; the tradition must be fulfilled.

"And when you come to us in the Great Mystery of the Hereafter, once more will we sit beneath your branches, and rest, and talk about the past.

"And the great bear who is my Brother will be there to listen.

"For we have been this long time kin together, you and I, and he.

"The Great Spirit is good and will not part us.

"No man, however wise, may say that only he shall live in the Kingdom of Hereafter.

"Till then, be strong, O my friend of many days.

"O Tree, O great bear, my Patrons, hear me.

"We will be waiting."

And then he ceased to speak, and fumbled in a pocket for awhile, and, pulling out a tiny wad of plug tobacco, pushed it into the brain-pan of the skull for an offering; though very carefully because the bone crumbled a little and pieces came away in his hands.

And the old Chief sat down, his back against the Tree that supported him but could not give him life; nor would have if it could. He remained very still, gazing out over the plains, listening to the Voice of the Tree, as the wind played among its topmost boughs, humming a deep, sustained and wavering note of unearthly beauty, as though picked from some wild, barbaric symphony; a chord that must have got its echo in Eternity.

Presently, as the aged man sat so quietly, the prairie lands grew dim and far away, so passed at last from his sight. And the Voice of the Tree was stilled. And the life of the old, old Indian passed on, as had that of the ancient silver-tip, two centuries ago, in this the chosen place of both of them.

And the Tree knew that the very last of its friends was gone, and that now it too must follow them. For this was the Fate of the Tree that those that loved it should die, while it lived on until none of them was left.

That night there came a storm, crashing down from the mountains; and in the tempest the lonely Tree moaned and wailed, and shook wildly on its foundations, and silhouetted against the white glare of the lightning it seemed to writhe, and to be contorted into shapes of agony.

IV

The next day a party of horsemen went by, discovered the body and buried it in a shallow, nameless grave beside the road. In an access of good spirits one of them took down the skull and threw it in the creek, among the tomato cans and other refuse that had gathered there.

Later it was decided to build a highway. Came engineers, hard practical men, skilled in their calling, who saw beauty in straight lines and rigid outlines and could view with complacency the fettering of primal forces that had run free for half a million years before man appeared at all, and who found romance in converting the face of Nature to man's needs. The old Sentinel at the gateway to the mountains stood in the line of least resistance, and was marked for destruction.

And the tree, that had lived too long, stood patiently and waited for the end. The first axe struck. The Tree gave no sign, but stood in all its grand composure and nobility to the last — and then swayed a little, and started on its journey to the ground. With a moaning, screaming cry, as its fibres ripped apart and its sweeping superstructure tore downwards through the air, the mighty conifer crashed to earth, down among the berries and the wild-flowers, prostrate on the pleasant mountain meadow where it first had sprung to life nearly seven hundred years before. And so the Fate of the Tree was finally accomplished, and the ancient tradition of the Blackfeet had been fulfilled at last.

And the mountains looked on in stony calmness; for they knew that trees must die and so must men, but that they live on for ever.

And as the final stroke was given and the life of the Tree was severed for all time, the figure of a naked Indian, crowned with a spreading eagle bonnet, stood for a fleeting instant high upon a ridge — and then was gone.

And beside him there had been the shaggy, monstrous shape of a gigantic grizzly bear.

V

An automobile, the finest that mechanical skill could make it, and with a full complement of those more or less useful gadgets so clever and expediently designed to render the latest models quickly obsolete, stimulating trade, was racing along the new highway through the mountains. It carried two passengers. The driver had sensitive, almost delicate hands and the quiet steady glance of the habitual observer. His companion, who sat beside him, was a gross man with heavy pouches under his eyes and a pendulous jowl. He had bulbous lips and his fingers supported a superfluity of rings. A cigar was cocked at a high angle in one corner of his mouth.

As the car sped on, it entered a mountain pass from the summit of which, looking back, there could be had a very fine view of the prairie farm lands. The driver brought the car to a stop, and looked about him with evident appreciation of the surroundings. "Gosh!" he exclaimed. "Take a look at those mountains! Great stuff, eh?"

The other chewed on his cigar and looked out speculatively at the looming peaks.

"Can't use them in my business," he asserted, adding "Poor lookin' country to me."

Beside the highway was an enormous jack-pine stump. The fat man removed his cigar and spat, forcefully and accurately, spattering the stump.

The car passed on.

A red squirrel raced across the highway with a pine-cone in his mouth, planted it somewhere in the meadow, and straightway forgot about it.

For a Salish Chief
Muriel Millen

The great outdoors became part of him.
His eyes had known the shadowed green
      of forest depths,
      the flash of dappled fawn in bracken,
      yellow sun on towering rocks;
      had seen the sparkle of mountain streams;
      the majestic march of combers
      on the open sea.
His ears were tuned to the eagle's cry,
      the chatter of the squirrel,
      the hum of myriad insect life.
He knew the muted call of the owl at dusk,
      the music in the woodland waterfall.

These to him were more than sight and sound;
      their imprints no mere surface etching.

Rather they were familiar, too,
　　as symbols of the spirit world,
　　a linking with the universe,
　　and part of the immemorial lore
　　of all his people.

But now the chief is dead.
Today he goes to make complete
　　his unity with Nature.

Alberta Memories
Bill Meilen

Here stand no stones . . .
　　No histrionic megaliths
　　Raised by the giants of the past . . .
Only the trees . . .
　　Murmuring in an unknown tongue
　　To tell us of the yesterdays
Of Canada . . .
　　But look into the face of Man . . .
　　The Cree, the Stoney and the Bloods
And you will see . . .
　　Read there the lines of memory
　　Carved in the faces of their old
By Time's chisel . . .
　　Catch them some day listening to
　　Whispering spirits of the wild
And you will know . . .
　　Hear them singing their song of loss
　　Throbbing drums of ancient nations
And wasted years . . .
　　Look into the waters of their eyes
　　For shadows of thundering hunts
On wide prairies . . .

Now all is gone like campfire smoke
Sifting between ebony bars
Of pine and fir . . .
    Start against a *cinnamon* sun
    When day has only just begun . . .
Here stand no stones . . .
    Except the lodgepoles of the sky
    Rising in mute testimony
To all that's gone.

The Big Fir
Roderick Haig-Brown

The description of the Big Fir has aroused so much interest that every year visitors call at the author's home on the banks of the Campbell River on Vancouver Island and ask to have this ancient tree pointed out to them.

August is a month of too much change for me to be altogether happy in it. The days of the first weeks are rich and golden, full of summer and life and warmth, of children planning and playing, people coming and going. But sometimes late in the month one becomes suddenly aware that summer is old and almost over, that it is nearly time for the children to go back to school, that asters are blooming, too many things are ripening, the leaves on the trees are set in a maturity already dry.

In a very real sense it is the year's passing, the culmination of all that built or rested under the fall rain and the winter snow, of spring's thrust and summer's bloom. Hot dry days of summer renewed are ahead in September, lively days of fall, and the pleasant, restful close in of winter. But there is that week or so of summer's lapse, of unwilling concession that another year is done. Mostly I think it is in the nearness of the children's return to another year of school, in the end of their summer's freedom. I like it less and less as the years go on.

When I feel this way I nearly always find myself thinking of the Big Fir. The Big Fir is not a true fir, but a Douglas fir, a false hemlock, the tree that has made the economy of British Columbia and the Pacific Northwest. It is the last true giant of its kind in all this flat near the river mouth, six feet in diameter breast high from the ground, and around two hundred feet tall. Judging by the rings on stumps of other trees on the flat, it is probably a little less than five hundred years old. It stands in the open field we call the Big Fir Field, nothing else near it except three or four of its own seedlings, the largest of them now thirty or forty feet high, standing so close that they seem part of the tree itself.

The Big Fir is slowly dying. It is dying because it is old, because it has a disease woodsmen call conk, and probably another disease called stump rot. Yet it is alive only because it is conky. The first loggers with their oxen passed it by for that reason more than fifty years ago; their skid road went through not three hundred feet from it and I cannot imagine their leaving it for any other reason. Other loggers passed that same way later, taking the lesser trees that the first loggers had left, but they still did not touch the Big Fir and its even larger companion which stood over by the barn. In 1922, when a crown fire struck down the far side of the river and leapt across on a northwest wind to a ridge a quarter of a mile away, fire fighters felled the tree by the barn. But they left the Big Fir standing.

The Big Fir itself has been touched by fire, so deeply touched that the eight-inch bark near the base is all burned away from the east side and the blackness of fire shows in crevices in the bark all round the tree. There are tentative axe marks here and there and many riflemen, at many times, have used the great trunk as a backstop for their target practice.

People often ask me why I don't cut down the Big Fir. "It's

dying,'' they say. ''Anyone can see that. And you'd get ten years good wood out of it.''

Sure it's dying. No one knows that better than I do. I've been watching it for nearly twenty years now. The wind-flattened top was green when I first knew the tree, sparse but green. One year life no longer reached that far up the tree, the needles died and fell away, then the little twigs fell away and after them the branchlets, then a branch or two, then some of the bark from the main trunk. But that all took five years or more. The topmost twenty feet of the tree are dead now and the tips of the lower branches are dying one by one, but there are seventy or eighty feet of heavy green limbs still above the lowest hundred feet of clear trunk. My guess is the tree has another fifty years of dying ahead of it, or somewhat more than I have. So long as any part of it is green I want it to stand.

The Big Fir was a good-sized tree before *Hamlet* was written and has managed to hold not only identity but life far longer than *Hamlet's* author held either. More human identities have been lost in every year of the tree's life than the tree itself has shed seeds, yet as trees go this one is not such a great age. Looking up at it against the sunset sky of an evening well on in August, remembering that it is almost time for the children to start school again, that another summer is past of the few remaining summers they will come free from school and go back to school, I feel the tree's pitiless permanence. It has used another year towards its death and during the year has scattered two or three hundred pounds of broken wood from its dead top about the field; yet even to my eye, it is scarcely changed.

I do not hate the tree or resent it or even wish it different. In most moods I love it and admire it. If it were young and vigorous, I think I should not even resent its permanence. If it is only just mortal, it is also only just living. But its enormous substance, lasting so long, yielding so little, seems to emphasize how short a time there is to look at things, to feel and know and think things. That the tree has been dying ever since I have known it and will still be dying after I am dead focuses my gloomier moods upon it; if only it wouldn't spread its last moments over my lifetime and beyond both ends I could accept it with nothing but happiness.

As it is, the Big Fir has many splendid moments. In spite of the dead top and the great blisters of the conk high on the trunk it remains magnificent. For over ten years, before I moved to this new room, my study window looked directly out at it. I used to watch its great green limbs moving slowly and easily in the southeast gales, against the clouds of the driven sky. The ducks pelt past it on such days and swing back into the wind. I have watched a hundred, perhaps a thousand, eagles perch in its topmost branches. I have seen it plastered with snow from ground to top, standing, tall and straight in the sunlight, green and brown and white against a blue and white sky. On a day like this I have watched blocks of snow fall away from the high branches, explode into the finest powder, and linger in a cloud of white all the way down the trunk.

I have watched flickers and pileated woodpeckers and downy woodpeckers search the crevices of the tree's bark for grubs. I have seen ravens in the tree and crows and many hawks. Early one morning, as I went over to the barn to milk, a great blue heron was perched on the dead top. I thought he would be the one I watched almost daily at his patient fishing in the eddy on the far side of the river. But then four others flew on slow wings from beyond the alders, circled the tree, and pitched there as the first one called to them. Three of the birds seemed clumsy and uncertain, and I judged them to be young ones. It is the only time I have seen five herons in any one tree, away from a heronry.

Once the Big Fir was shaded by other trees as large and larger, packed all about it in the heavy forest. The Indians had a smoke house within a hundred feet of it then and beached their canoes within reach of its shadow. I have found myself fishing and swimming and planting seeds in the same shadow, and I have sheltered new-born lambs and nursed them to life in its lee. The first trail up the river passed near it and the first skid road and the first wagon road. It is only a mass of wood, pitch-seamed, diseased, and rotten, with no more than a spark of giant life remaining in a narrow strip of sapwood. There are probably a million other great trees like it on Vancouver Island, overmature, moribund, without significance except perhaps in the seed they throw. Only a sentimentalist could give importance to such a thing. Yet I shall look up at the Big Fir a thousand times or more before I die, and never without emotion.

Death of a Giant

Bruce Hutchison

A man with a mechanical saw attacked a huge Douglas fir tree near here today and quickly felled the work of several centuries. I counted the annual rings of growth on the butt and reached a total of 703 when those circular lines, the record of recent times, became too thin for the naked eye.

Through something over 703 years that tree had stood indestructible, until a revolving belt of steel ended its labours in less than half an hour. The man with the saw said that the tree stood in the way of his new garage and had to be removed.

He is a practical man, not given much to speculation and careless of history. But any historian would have found food for thought in the spectacle of that mighty stump, cleanly severed, and the prostrate mass of wood — enough material to build a house which might last, with care, for a single lifetime.

King John must have been signing a certain document on the island of Runnymede about the time when a seed sprouted on an unknown continent and a tiny sprig of green thrust itself up, among many others, from the floor of the jungle.

When Columbus discovered the new world the seedling had become a tree two and a half centuries old, had hardly reached its prime, was just getting into its stride and stood a mere hundred feet high.

When an English axe was severing the neck of a Stuart king the tree, safe from any axe stroke, was approaching healthy middle age. It had begun to decline at the time of Waterloo.

How often the tree had grasped the spring wind and transformed it into the music of the first harp, shredded it through innumerable fingers in the rustle and dry tick of summer and uttered the organ tones of the winter gale when no ear was present to hear it!

How many billion tons of water were sucked from the earth over the years and hoisted into the trunk and limbs no mathematician can calculate. How the tree extracted the soil's chemicals and rendered them into bark, cambium layer, heartwood and green needles no scientist has been able to guess. How such a frame could stand upright in the storms of seven hundred winters or support an overpowering load of snow on nothing but a frail network of roots no engineer or architect can imagine.

It could not have been an easy business. Around one tree stronger than its fellows countless competitors raised their heads briefly, withered in the shade of the giant and died. It ate their mouldering bodies with ravenous appetite and converted them again into living wood. Nothing but man could threaten that massive organism.

Man arrived late in the tree's life. The first human eye to see it doubtless belonged to some wandering Indian whose stone axe was too blunt to use on such formidable fuel. Then came a white logger with a steel axe, a cross-cut saw and a team of oxen, and he left his little mark. The gash of his axe remained on the trunk, almost covered over by the spreading bark. After a few futile strokes he had left the tree as too large for his tools, too heavy for his oxen. Later on some hunter had driven a spike into the wood, perhaps to hang up a deer while he skinned it. His spike had rusted away and broke in my fingers.

Nothing but modern man, with his high intelligence and cunning implements, could end the life of seven hundred years. This he proceeded to do and finished the job in twenty minutes by my watch. The tree swayed with a scream of torn wood and wings outstretched. The man who felled it was well pleased with his work. He could now drive his car conveniently into the new garage.

The Forest Fire
Bertrand Sinclair

That night Hollister wakened out of a sound sleep to sniff the air that streamed in through his open windows. It was heavy with the pungent odour of smoke. He rose and looked out. The silence of night lay on the valley, over the dense forest across the river, upon the fir-swathed southern slope. No leaf stirred. Nothing moved. It was still as death. And in this hushed blackness — lightencd only by a pale streak in the north and east that was the reflection of snowy mountain crests standing stark against the sky-line — this smoky wraith crept along the valley floor. No red glow greeted Hollister's sight. There was nothing but the smell of burning wood, that acrid, warm, heavy odour of smoke, the invisible herald of fire. It might be over the next ridge. It might be in the mouth of the valley. It might be thirty miles distant. He went back to bed, to lie with that taint of smoke in his nostrils, thinking of Doris and the boy, of himself, of Charlie Mills, of Myra, of Archie Lawanne. He saw ghosts in that dusky chamber, ghosts of other days, and trooping on the heels of these came apparitions of a muddled future — until he fell asleep again, to be awakened at last by a hammering on his door.

The light of a flash-lamp revealed a logger from the Carr

settlement below. The smoke was rolling in billows when Hollister stepped outside. Down toward the Inlet's head there was a red flare in the sky.

"We got to get everybody out to fight that," the man said. "She started in the mouth of the river last night. If we don't check it and the wind turns right, it'll clean the whole valley. We sent a man to pull your crew off the hill."

In the growing dawn Hollister and the logger went down through the woods thick with smoke. They routed Lawanne out of his cabin, and he joined them eagerly. He had never seen a forest fire. What bore upon the woodsmen chiefly as a malignant, destructive force affected Lawanne as something that promised adventure, as a spectacle which aroused his wonder, his curious interest in vast, elemental forces unleashed. They stopped at Bland's and pressed him into service.

In an hour they were deployed before the fire, marshalled to the attack under men from Carr's, woodsmen experienced in battle against the red enemy, this spoiler of the forest with his myriad tongues of flame and breath of suffocating smoke.

In mid-summer the night airs in those long inlets and deep valleys move always toward the sea. But as the day grows and the sun swings up to its zenith, there comes a shift in the aerial currents. The wind follows the course of the sun until it settles in the westward, and sometimes rises to a gale. It was that rising of the west wind that the loggers feared. It would send the fire sweeping up the valley. There would be no stopping it. There would be nothing left in its wake but the blackened earth, smoking roots, and a few charred trunks standing gaunt and unlovely amid the ruin.

So now they strove to create a barrier which the fire should not pass. It was not a task to be perfunctorily carried on, there was no time for malingering. There was a very real incitement to great effort. Their property was at stake; their homes and livelihood; even their lives, if they made an error in the course and speed of the fire's advance and were trapped.

They cut a lane through the woods straight across the valley floor from the river to where the southern slope pitched sharply down. They felled the great trees and dragged them aside with powerful donkey engines to manipulate their gear. They cleared away the brush and the dry windfalls until this lane was bare as a travelled road — so that when the fire ate its way to this barrier there was a clear space in which should fall harmless the sparks and embers flung ahead by the wind.

There, at this labour, the element of the spectacular vanished. They could not attack the enemy with excited cries, with brandished weapons. They could not even see the enemy. They could hear him, they could smell the resinous odour of his breath. That was all. They laid their defences against him with methodical haste, chopping, heaving, hauling the steel cables here and there from the donkeys, sweating in the blanket of heat that overlaid the woods, choking in the smoke that rolled above them and about them. And always in each man's mind ran the uneasy thought of the west wind rising.

But throughout the day the west wind held its breath. The flames crawled, ate their way instead of leaping hungrily. The smoke rose in dun clouds above the burning area and settled in grey vagueness all through the woods, drifting in wisps, in streamers, in fantastic curlings, pungent, acrid, choking the men. The heat of the fire and the heat of a summer sun, in a windless sky, made the valley floor a sweat-bath in which the loggers worked stripped to undershirts and overalls, blackened with soot and grime.

Night fell. The fire had eaten the heart out of a block half a mile square. It was growing. A redness brightened the sky. Lurid colours fluttered above the hottest blaze. A flame would run with incredible agility up the trunk of a hundred-foot cedar to fling a yellow banner from the topmost boughs, to colour the billowing smoke, the green of near-by trees, to wave and gleam and shed coruscating spark-showers and die down again to a dull glow.

Through the short night the work went on. Here and there a

man's weariness grew more than he could bear, and he would lie down to sleep for an hour or two. They ate food when it was brought to them. Always, while they could keep their feet, they worked.

Hollister worked on stoically into the following night, keeping Lawanne near him, because it was all new and exciting to Lawanne, and Hollister felt that he might have to look out for him if the wind took any sudden, dangerous shift.

But the mysterious forces of the air were merciful. During the twenty-four hours there was nothing but little vagrant breezes, and the drafts created by the heat of the fire itself. When day came again, without striking a single futile blow at the heart of the fire, they had drawn the enemy's teeth and clipped his claws — in so far as the flats of the Toba were threatened. The fire would burn up to that cleared path and burn itself out — with men stationed along to beat out each tiny flame that might spring up by chance. And when that was done, they rested on their oars, so to speak; they took time to sit down and talk without once relaxing their vigilance.

In a day or two the fire would die out against that barrier, always provided the west wind did not rise and in sportive mockery fling showers of sparks across to start a hundred little fires burning in the woods behind their line of defence. A forest fire was never beaten until it was dead. The men rested, watched, patrolled their line. They looked at the sky and sighed for rain. A little knot of them gathered by a tree. Someone had brought a box of sandwiches, a pail of coffee and tin cups. They gulped the coffee and munched the food and stretched themselves on the soft moss. Through an opening they could see a fiery glow topped by wavering sheets of flame. They could hear the crackle and snap of burning wood.

"A forest fire is quite literally hell, isn't it?" Lawanne asked.

Hollister nodded. His eyes were on Bland. The man sat on the ground. He had a cup of coffee in one hand, a sandwich in the other. He was blackened almost beyond recognition, and he was viewing with patent disgust the state of his clothes and particularly of his hands. He set down his food and rubbed at his fingers with a soiled handkerchief. Then he resumed eating and drinking. It appeared to him a matter of necessity rather than a thing from which he derived any satisfaction. Near him Charlie Mills lay stretched on the moss, his head pillowed on his folded arms, too weary to eat or drink, even at Hollister's insistence.

"Dirty job this, eh?" Bland remarked. "I'll appreciate a bath. Phew! I shall sleep for a week when I get home."

By mid-afternoon of the next day, Sam Carr decided they had the fire well in hand and so split his forces, leaving half on guard and letting the others go home to rest. Hollister's men remained on the spot in case they were needed; he and Lawanne and Bland went home.

But that was not the end of the great blaze. Blocked in the valley the fire, as if animated by some deadly purpose, crept into the mouth of a bushy canyon and ran up hill with demonic energy until it was burning fiercely over a benchland to the west of Hollister's timber.

The fight began once more. With varying phases it raged for a week. They would check it along a given line and rest for awhile, thinking it safely under control. Then a light shift of wind would throw it across their line of defence, and in a dozen places the forest would break into flame. The fire worked far up the slope, but its greatest menace lay in its steady creep westward. Slowly it ate up to the very edge of Hollister's timber, in spite of all their checks, their strategy, the prodigious effort of every man to check its vandal course.

Then the west wind, which had held its breath so long broke loose with unrestrained exhalation. It fanned the fire to raging fury, sent it leaping in yellow sheets through the woods. The blaze lashed eagerly over the tops of the trees, the dreaded crown fire of the North Woods. Where its voice had been a whisper, it became a roar, an ominous, warning roar to which the loggers gave instant heed and got themselves and their gear off that timbered slope.

They could do no more. They had beaten it in the valley. Backed by the lusty presence of the west wind, it drove them off the hill and went its wanton way unhindered.

In the flat by Hollister's house the different crews came together. There was not one of them but drooped with exhaustion. They sat about on the parched ground, on moss, against tree trunks, and stared upon the hill.

Already the westerly gale had cleared the smoke from the lower valley. It brought a refreshing coolness off the salt water, and it was also baring to their sight the spectacular destruction of the forest.

All that area where Hollister's cedars had stood was a red chaos out of which great flames leaped aloft and waved snaky tongues, blood-red, molten gold, and from which great billows of smoke poured away to wrap in obscurity all the hills beyond. There was nothing they could do now. They watched it apathetically, too weary to care.

Hollister looked on the destruction of his timber most stolidly of all. For days he had put forth his best effort. His body ached. His eyes smarted. His hands were sore. He had done his best without enthusiasm. He was not oppressed so greatly as were some of these men by this vast and useless destruction. What did it matter, after all? A few trees more or less! A square mile or two of timber out of that enormous stand. It was of no more consequence in the sum total than the life of some obscure individual in the teeming millions of the earth. It was his timber. So was his life a possession peculiar to himself. And neither seemed greatly to matter; neither did matter greatly to anyone but himself.

It was all a muddle. He was very tired, too tired to bear thinking, almost too tired to feel. He was conscious of himself as a creature of weariness sitting against a tree, his scarred face blackened like the tired faces of these other men, wondering dully what was the sum of all this sweat and strain, the shattered plans, the unrewarded effort, the pain and stress that men endure. A man made plans and they failed. He bred hope in his soul and saw it die. He longed for and sought his desires, always to see them vanish like a mirage, just as they seemed within his grasp.

Lawanne and Bland had gone home, dragging themselves on tired limbs. Carr's men rested where they chose. They must watch lest the fire back down into the valley again and destroy their timber as it had destroyed Hollister's. They had blankets and food. Hollister gave his own men the freedom of the house. Their quarters on the hill stood in the doomed timber. The old log house would be ashes now. . . .

He found his chin sinking on his breast. He roused himself and walked over to the house. His men were sprawled on the rugs, sleeping in grotesque postures. Hollister picked his way among them. Almost by the door of his bedroom Charlie Mills sprawled on his back, his head resting on a sofa cushion. He opened his eyes as Hollister passed.

"That was a tough game," Hollister said.

"It's all a tough game," Mills answered wearily and cl   h d his eyes again.

Hollister went on into the room. He threw himself across the bed. In ten seconds he was fast asleep.

The Alders

Peter Trower

The alders are the reoccupiers
they come easily
and quick into skinned land —
rising like an ambush
and raked ridges —
jabbing like whiskers up through the washedout
faces of neverused roads.

The alders are the forestfixers
bandaging brown wounds
with applegreen sashes —
filling in for the fallen
firs —
jostling up by the stumps
of grandfather cedars —
leaning slim to the wind
by logjammed
loggerleft streams.

The alders are the encroachers
seizing ground the greater trees owned
once
but no more.

It is the time of the alders
they come
like a bright upstart army
crowding the deadwood spaces —
reaching
at last for the hand of the whole
unshadowed sun.

Nature
Answers

The Music of Nature
Patricia Armstrong

In natural music all the lakes and fields
The marshes and the wilderness abound;
And through the brotherhood that binds our earth
Each melody (rough, sweet or muted) wakes
    A kindred feeling in humanity:

Who strolls at dusk along a reedy marsh
Can hearken to the husky trill of frogs
    How quickly hushed to stillness by footfall;
A daylight stroller stops to hear, entranced,
Three seeking notes before the burbling lilt
    Cascading from a post-perched meadowlark;
On prairie farms the gopher from his mound
    Sends forth his shrill, clear whistle in the sun;
And trees have music notes of which not least
    The fluttering sigh of poplar leaves wind-tossed.

But to awake a primitive response
Dredged back to life from some primeval deep,
Beneath all thought and reason far beyond,
    For me the repertoire of Nature keeps:
The ululating waver of a loon
    Questing at dawn from unknown lake to lake;
Or in the night below a drifting moon
Coyote yodelling from a far-off hill,
Echoed about by melancholy howls
    Beyond dim bluffs deep in a barley field.

Food from the Flora

Bradford Angier

One day you may be boating down the Peace River near the start of its more-than-2,000-mile journey, inland to Great Slave Lake and thence as the Mackenzie to the Arctic Ocean. Soon after the headwaters of this wilderness highway mingle in the Rocky Mountain Trench, the river turns abruptly eastward to flow through the backbone of the Canadian Rockies. If you will watch the left shore after chuting through the minor turbulence known as Finlay Rapids, your eyes will likely as not catch the platinum gleam of Lost Cabin Creek.

Here it was, at the turn of the century, during those apical days on the world's gold-fever chart, that four prospectors shared the still-standing cabin from which the stream has taken its name. Their grubstake dwindling, three watched with growing helplessness the first of their number die, by which time the survivors themselves had become so feeble that they lacked the vigour to open the frozen ground outside.

They buried their companion in the only spot they could find earth still loose enough to dig. A second "gravel-puncher" died and had also to be buried. Before the fourth succumbed, he had by himself managed to scoop out enough of a grave so that a third emaciated body could join the others already beneath the cabin floor.

Yet as you will be able to testify from what you can see while boating past Lost Cabin Creek, and as I can substantiate from having lived in the vicinity for years, the wilderness there abounds the year round with wild edibles.

Hundreds of wild foods enhance North American fields and woodlands, mountains and canyons, deserts, shores, and certainly the swamplands. The inner bark of the familiar *birches* is pleasantly sweet and sustaining. Even birch sap is refreshing.

As for young birch leaves and twigs, the soft formative tissue between wood and bark, and the thin bark covering the roots, any of these steeped in hot water make a favorite backwoods tea having the perfume and flavour of wintergreen.

The lodgepole and other *pines* have an eatable inner bark that is preferred fresh by some and sun-dried by others. There are even those gourmets who claim it is at its best only when scraped from the south side of a young tree while the spring sap is rising.

The new emerald tufts that brighten the various *conifers* in the spring are best for the spicy brew known as spruce tea. One way to make this beverage is to push as many of the youngest available needles of such evergreens as the pine, spruce, fir, and hemlock into boiling water which is then set off the fire to steep. The drink will both prevent and cure scurvy, although for this purpose it's better to eat the starchy needles directly. The tender young ones have a mild and pleasant flavour and chew up quickly. *Rose hips* also can be a particularly valuable part of a wilderness diet because of their abundant Vitamin C which both averts and cures scurvy.

The younger one is, the more irresistible the various *wild cherries* seem to be, especially when raw. Adults come to prefer gathering the more astringent of these green for jelly making, and ripe for boiling with an added sweet for table syrup. *Elderberries* are fairly widely recognized. The dry, bland, reddish *bearberry* is edible although practically tasteless.

The salad plants and potherbs growing wild on this continent are particularly abundant. For example, the entire young plant of the *dandelion* is relished raw in salads and, especially when older, after it has been boiled just enough to render it tender. To many the clean bitter tang is stimulating. Those who do not care for it can discard the first water and finish the cooking in fresh fluid. I've also gathered dandelion roots in the fall, allowed them to dry, roasted them in the oven, and finally ground the shriveled dark shapes remaining. It is a widely used coffee stretcher. Put in cold water and slowly brought to a boil, it is not a bad wilderness coffee substitute, either.

Even more generally known in this respect are the correspondingly processed roots of the closely related *chicory* whose similarly prepared and eaten young leaves, forming about the base of the plant, are often mistaken for dandelion. From its stout taproot, chicory develops into a tall, widely known weed with large, usually blue, flowers

Some of the common edibles, such as *skunk cabbage,* are plagued by psychological handicaps similar to that which bans roast muskrat from many a table. Actually the succulent dark meat of the muskrat is pretty hard to equal . . . when served as musquash or swamp rabbit. And so it is with many wild greens. Young skunk cabbage, for one, becomes tender and blandly delicious when boiled in several changes of water. The skunk cabbage, which grows in moist and usually shady areas, early in the year pushed up its shell-like sheath in which rises a fleshy spike embedded with numerous tiny flowers. Veins are very evident on the large, succulent leaves which are best for eating when they first appear. An emergency flour, incidentally, can be made from the rootstocks which are fleshy and threaded with many side-rootlets. These roots are dried and ground, their somewhat peppery taste diminishing in pungency after a week or two. Indians hurried the process by first roasting these intact in pits.

Pigweed is to many palates the pick of the wild greens, especially when dished up as *lamb's quarter* which is one of its most formal names. Its widespread prolificness and mild flavour make it one of the more important wild foods. The stem is covered with longish, pale green leaves with irregular edges, from whose shape has come the name of *goosefoot.* The small green flowers appear in long, thick clusters that later turn to tiny dark seeds.

Stalk, leaves, flowers, and grains of the pigweed are all

nourishing both raw and cooked. Even when a small vegetable garden is in full production near our home in the woods at Hudson's Hope, British Columbia, we often bypass it to gather instead young pigweed thriving nearby.

The seeds, like those of the *green amaranth* which is also called pigweed, occasionally help to relieve whatever monotony there may be in bannock and other breadstuffs, lending them a caraway-seed effect. They can also be dried and ground for use as meal.

The widely distributed *nettle* is one of the most delicately flavoured of all greens. Leather gloves and a knife take all the sting out of gathering them, and they are at their best when only a few inches tall. You can get along all right, too, by using two sticks as tongs. Nettles, you might expect, would require lengthy cooking. However, the young shoots need only be dropped into a container of boiling water that may then be set away from the heat. As soon as the dark greens have cooled enough to be eaten, they may be forked out and served.

Milkweed, which in the fall bursts its long rough pods and sends its seeds soaring in white fluff, is at its best as a food in the spring. You'll probably want to change the boiling water several times to eliminate the milky sap (from which, incidentally, a sort of rubber can be manufactured). After the milkweed has simmered until tender in a final portion of salted water, drain and serve with some edible grease such as bacon drippings. The flowers are good, particularly when you're hankering for something sweet. Later on, the young seed pods are also boiled and eaten. Indians relished the cooked roots.

Miner's lettuce, a salad plant whose crisp leaves and stems may also be boiled as greens, is notably easy to distinguish. Anyone who does not know it already, has only to look for a small green plant with flower stems growing from a short mass of leaves at ground level. The clinching feature is that part way up each stem a pair of leaves grow together so as to form a sort of cup through whose middle the stalk continues.

Wild growths are not anything to take chances with. Some, like the apparently innocuous *buttercup,* are poisonous when taken internally.

No antidote has yet been discovered for certain poisonous *mushrooms,* which are all the more lethal because in many cases no ill symptoms are manifested until half a day or so after eating. The only poisonous wild growth in the Arctic happens to be a mushroom. Because at best mushrooms anywhere are extremely low in caloric value, it is a sound idea to avoid them entirely as an emergency food unless you already know them well.

On the other hand, some of the unlikeliest weeds can be safely eaten by man. The young stalks of both flowers and leaves of the common *burdock* may be peeled and devoured either raw or boiled. *Russian thistle,* the West's most familiar tumbleweed, boils up into a savory green if gathered while it is just coming up.

Then there are the fruits and fleshy segments of the North American varieties of *cacti* which, once they have been unarmed, lend themselves surprisingly well to every sort of table use from serving raw to roasting and even frying. These are found not only in the desert but in dry and rocky localities throughout the continent and in sandy soil even along such northern rivers as the Peace beside which I've lived for most of the past dozen years. Especially in arid regions, the sweetish watery sap in a few of the larger plants is enough to be vital in emergencies.

Perhaps the most widely known of the wild foods of the far North is the lichen known as *rock tripe,* whose habitat reaches into the southern states. Rock tripe resembles a leathery dark lettuce leaf, up to about three inches wide, attached at its center to a rocky surface. Unless the day is wet, rock tripe is apt to be rather dry. It can be eaten raw, but much of the time users prefer it boiled to thicken soups and stews.

Reindeer moss, whose range also extends into the United

States, is another edible lichen. It resembles moss, however, being a low greyish-green plant with a quantity of many-branched stems instead of leaves. *Iceland moss,* another eatable lichen and not a moss, is found as far south as the States. It is comparable to reindeer moss, being a brownish-green plant whose numerous flat branches turn in to create a tube-like effect.

A bitter lichen such as Iceland moss is first boiled or soaked to remove the cause of the bitterness — an acid which although not poisonous, is sometimes nauseous and may cause severe internal irritation. After being dried, the lichen is powdered, perhaps merely by being rubbed between the palms. The resulting flour is sometimes used to stretch ordinary flour. It is often utilized "as is" for making breadstuffs. I like it in bannock. The flour is also resoaked and then boiled to gruel-like and jelly-like consistencies which by themselves are short on taste but surpassingly long on nourishment.

These few notes go to show that food, free for the taking, is abundant in the Canadian wilderness, if only one knows what to eat, and how to eat it.

Picketing Supermarkets

Tom Wayman

Because all this food is grown in the store
do not take the leaflet.
Cabbages, broccoli and tomatoes
are raised at night in the aisles.
Milk is brewed in the rear storage areas.
Beef produced in vats in the basement.
Do not take the leaflet.
Peanut butter and soft drinks
are made fresh each morning by store employees.

Our oranges and grapes
are so fine and round
that when held up to the lights they cast no shadow.
Do not take the leaflet.

And should you take one
do not believe it.
This chain of stores has no connection
with anyone growing food someplace else.
How could we have an effect on local farmers?
Do not believe it.

The sound here is Muzak, for your enjoyment.
It is not the sound of children crying.
There *is* a lady offering samples
to mark Canada Cheese Month.
There is no dark-skinned man with black hair beside her
wanting to show you the inside of a coffin.
You would not have to look if there was.
And there are no Nicaraguan heroes
in any way connected with the bananas.

Pay no attention to these people.
The manager is a citizen.
All this food is grown in the store.

Red Man's Remedies
Kerry Wood

An Indian has been in our town's hospital these last ten days, rushed in from the west country suffering a ruptured appendix. The operation was successful, and Jim is now ready to leave for his log cabin home again, a wonderful constitution helping him make a quick recovery.

His name is Jim Yelloweyes, a non-treaty Cree Indian who

lives in the back-bush country south west of Rocky Mountain House, Alberta. A pretty fine type of Indian, Jim, well educated and thoroughly independent and proud of it. Good friends of his at the Mountain House town had heard of his sickness and called a doctor, and the doctor's diagnosis made them rush him in to our hospital for the necessary operation.

With his dark head silhouetted against the white linen of the hospital bed, Jim stared around with his eager eyes and asked many questions. All this was new to him. As friendship grew, we asked questions in return, and we learned many things about Indian methods of treating sickness.

Jim had been waiting the arrival of his chief when the doctor visited his cabin.

"The chief is our medicine man," Jim explained.

"Yes, but a medicine man couldn't have cured you of this sickness, could he?"

Jim smiled and shook his head.

"Maybe not the present day medicine man," he answered. "Today, our chiefs tell us to listen to the white man doctor when it is a sickness like this one. But in the old days, the old-time medicine man would have looked after me all right."

"But this was a serious sickness you had, Jim — a ruptured appendix always requires an operation."

He smiled again.

"In the old days before the white man came, we had medicine men who were wise about these things too. They kept small sharp knives, and sometimes they would cut away sick parts when a man got bad sick."

This amazed us, for we had not heard that the old medicine men were capable of understanding the intricate details of a major operation. Jim assured us that it was true, however, and so we had many more questions to ask. For instance, what did the patient do during the course of the operation — suffer the pain consciously?

"Our doctors give an anaesthetic, Jim; that is, they put you to sleep so that you will not feel the pain. What did the old Indians do?"

Jim was silent for a little while, wondering how he could explain himself to us so that he would be understood.

"My father told me these things about the old-time medicine men," he said. "And my father told me that when they used their knives on a man's body to cure sickness, the man did not feel pain. Before they cut, the medicine man looked a long time into the sick man's eyes, and he spoke quiet words, and sometimes put a hand on the sick man's head and rubbed it gently. Then when the time came for the medicine man to take his knives and cut, the sick one felt no pain. Maybe you cannot understand, but it was so."

Hypnotism? What else?

Then we asked Jim about other sicknesses, and about the methods used by the medicine men today. He gave us a long list, and told us about the uses the people of his tribe make of barks and roots found in the mountain country. Outdoorsmen will find these remedies interesting, and it may be that some of them will prove useful when someone falls sick in camp.

A common nose-bleed, for instance, can be instantly stopped by the simple process of breathing a little of the powdery dust of a dry puff-ball up the nostrils.

For a sore throat or a cough, the inner bark of chokecherry provides a fine medicine. Two big handfulls of the inner bark is placed in a sizeable pot of water and soaked overnight, then boiled hard for two hours. A large spoonful three times daily will soon clear up the throat condition.

"It is good, too, for sicknesses in the chest," Jim said. "In my language, we call it the lung medicine."

Saskatoon bark also has good medicinal qualities. The whole bark is used, placed thickly in a pot of water and boiled until the water is colored. This water is then used to wash wounds, Jim claiming that it hastened healing. It soothes pain in a bruise too, and is generally useful in the treatment of all cuts, aches, or bruises.

Another wound dressing that Jim thought outstanding was the pitch from the balsam spruce that grows in the heavier mountain forests. This pitch is used directly on the wound without any preparation, as a natural salve. Jim believed that Indians of the mountain country made more use of this balsam pitch than of any other Indian medicine. If a man knifed his finger or got a rope burn or had his leg skinned against a tree while riding, he simply smeared the sore spot with the balsam pitch and let it go at that.

"It is a strong cure," Jim said. "It keeps the wound clean too, and keeps away any poison."

The balsam pitch is also used for sex ailments, taken internally.

Fevers have a medicine that is nearly always available — Willow bark. The bark is ground to a pulp and soaked overnight in a pot of water, then boiled down to a third of its initial quantity. This brew is taken four times daily, a large spoonful at a time. Roots of the "Red Willow" or shrub variety of dogwood that grows in most parts of the west provide another good fever cure. The roots are carefully cleaned and then boiled in a large amount of water and used hot. Chills, severe colds, and bad fevers are among the sicknesses treated with these two remedies.

The white part of poplar bark makes a strong laxative. It is pulped and then boiled for three hours hard and the brew is taken in small spoonfuls sparingly.

Jim even had a sure-fire Spring Tonic to tell about. A couple of generous handfuls of black alder bark is used to make tea, boiled until one fourth of the original water amount is left. A half cupful of this concoction three times a day will do wonders in the springtime when pimples and skin eruptions tell that there is an unhealthy condition existing in the body. It is good for the whole system, Jim avowed.

Red Man's Remedies 273

As a last remedy, Jim spoke of the Juniper berries that are so easily gathered on the mountain slopes. A few dozen of these, brewed in tea form, make a powerful medicine to be used by those suffering with kidney troubles.

This had a familiar sound. Most of our kidney medicines have a good touch of juniper extract in them, and this was told to Jim.

"Sure!" he said, smiling. "Wise white men know that the Indians know what's good!"

Fire-Flowers
E. Pauline Johnson

And only where the forest fires have sped,
    Scorching relentlessly the cool north lands,
A sweet wild flower lifts its purple head,
And, like some gentle spirit sorrow-fed,
    It hides the scars with almost human hands.

And only to the heart that knows of grief,
    Of desolating fire, of human pain,
There comes some purifying sweet belief,
Some fellow-feeling beautiful, if brief.
    And life revives, and blossoms once again.

Caught Up in Colors
Lorraine Meaker

Like colored tissue paper
blowing in the wind,
or a golden satin scarf
fluttering violently on
a clothesline
the butterfly struggles
in the spider's web

The Acrobat
Ann Lazechko

the early morning sunlight
touches a band
of dewdrops,
and draws my attention
to a silent
little acrobat
who glides across
his lacy web —
then soars
through the air on a
single
silver
strand
until he lands,
at last,
in the centre of
his
wildflower stage.

The Owl
Mark Bailey

A forest, dark and bare stands
in the light of the rising moon.
Grim and silent stands
while shafts of shimmering, liquid
brilliance
pour through the maze of its limbs.
A solitary note of absolute music,
meaningless in its depth,
wavers and falls.

A mouse, shy and cautious,
advances into the world
inquisitive, and starts off.
Too late it notices the soundless,
casual shadow.
Petrified with terror, it begins to run,
filled with the knowledge of futility.
With casual uninterest the shadow
overtakes and snatches.
The terror is gone, only a giddy
fascination.

The shadow flies away, knowing
that sooner or later everything
is caught.

The House of McGinnis
Grey Owl

A loud thud, a crash, the tinkle of broken glass, then silence. A
sound as of a hand-saw being run at great speed by an expert, a
bumping, dragging noise and a vicious rattling; then another
crash; more silence.

"And what," asked my guest as we neared the camp, "is
that; an earthquake?"

"That," I answered, with some misgiving, "is the beaver,
the ones you are coming to see!"

We entered the cabin, and the scene within was something
to be remembered, the devastation resembling that left in the
wake of a young whirlwind. The table was down, and the
utensils it had held had disappeared; a four-foot stick of wood
protruded through a shattered window, and below the one that
remained a quantity of wood had been piled, affording facilities
for the effective use of a battering ram. The washstand had been

dissected and neatly piled in the bunk from which the blankets had been removed, these being included in a miscellany of articles such as dishes, moccasins, and so forth, with which the stove was barricaded. With hurried apologies to my visitor I assessed the damage, but beyond the disarrangements just mentioned, there was no serious harm done; that is, so far, no lives had been lost. I had been away two days, being delayed by soft weather, which, with its exhilarating effect on these animals accounted for the delirious attack on my humble fixtures.

There was no sign of the raiders, they having retreated to their house at the presence of a stranger; but later they appeared and were introduced, and again retired, hopping and capering like little round gnomes, taking with them the peace offerings of chocolate and apples which they accepted, after considerable diplomatic manoeuvring from my companion.

McGinty and McGinnis, having put their house in order, were receiving from five to half past, the guest providing the luncheon.

Only those who have had the opportunity of studying living specimens over an extended period can obtain any idea of the almost human mentality of these likeable little creatures. Destructive they are and their activities have much the same effect on the camp that two small animated sawmills running loose would have. They resemble an army tank, being built on much the same lines, and progressing in a similar manner, over or through anything that is in the way. After the first six months they can sink themselves through a six-inch log at a remarkable speed, biting lengthways with the grain of the wood for three or four inches, cutting the cross section at each end and pulling out the chip.

They roam around the camp, and, with no evil intent but apparently from just sheer joy of living, take large slices out of table-legs, and chairs, and nice long splinters out of the walls, and their progress is marked by little piles and strings of chips.

The House of McGinnis 277

This is the fore part of the evening. After 'lights out' the more serious work commences, such as the removal of deerskin rugs, the transferring of firewood from behind the stove into the middle of the floor, or the improvement of some waterproof footwear by the addition of a little openwork on the soles. They will gnaw a hole in a box of groceries to investigate, and are very fond of toilet soap.

In winter they will not leave the camp and I sink a small bath tub in the floor for them, as they need water constantly. They make a practice of lying in the tub eating their sticks and birch tops, later climbing into the bunk to dry themselves. To accomplish this they sit upright and squeeze and scrub the entire body. The water never penetrates beyond the guard hairs into the fur, but I suppose half a pint is no exaggeration of the amount of water one of them will squeeze out of his coat.

It is remarkable that in spite of the orgy of destruction that went on for the first two weeks in camp, the door, an easy target, was not molested, and nothing was cut that would occasion an air leak into the camp. It is their nature to bank up against the intrusion of cold, and any loose materials that they could gather would be piled along the foot of the door, where there was a certain amount of draught. They barred the door so effectively on one occasion that I had to remove a window to enter the cabin.

Some mornings, at daylight, I would awaken to find one on each side of me sleeping, lying on their backs snoring like any human. At intervals during sleep they sharpen their teeth in readiness for the next onslaught. When working, if the teeth do not seem to be in good shape, they pause for half a minute or so and sharpen them, repeating this until they are suited. The skull is fitted with a longitudinal slot which allows for the necessary motion of the jaws, and the resultant grinding is much like the whetting of an axe. The sound of an axe or knife being filed struck them with terror, and they would drop everything and run to me for protection, evidently thinking the noise came from some large animal whetting its teeth.

Beaver are the most persevering creatures I know of, man not excepted, and any job which they undertake is never abandoned until completed or proved impossible. They conduct their operations with all the serious intentness and economy of movement of trained artisans, and at the conclusion of each stage, small adjustments are made, and little pats and pushes given, either expressing satisfaction with the work or testing its solidity, I know not which.

These queer little people are also good housekeepers. Branches brought in for their feed are immediately seized on and piled to one side of the entrance to their abode. After feeding on pancakes or bread pudding, which they dearly love, the dish is pushed away into some far corner, along with the peeled sticks and other unused portions of feed. Their beds, consisting of sacks, which they tear to shreds, mixed with shredded birch-bark and long, very fine shavings cut from the floor, after being used for a period, are brought out and scattered on the floor, apparently to dry, and taken in again after a couple of days. They spend long periods on their toilet. One of the toes of the webbed hind feet is jointed so as to bend in any direction, and is fitted with a kind of double claw; with this they comb their entire coat.

They seem capable of great affection, which they show by grasping my clothing with their strong forepaws, very hands in function, pushing their heads into some corner of my somewhat angular personality, bleating and whimpering. At times they clamour for attention, and if taken notice of they shake their heads from side to side, rolling on their backs with squeals of joy. If left alone for as long as twenty-four hours, on my return they are very subdued until I talk to them, when they at once commence their uncouth gambols and their queer wrestling.

They conduct these wrestling matches — for they can be

called nothing else — by rising on their hind feet, supported by the tail, while the forepaws are locked in neck and underarm holds, looking like dancers. In this position they strain and push, each striving to overcome the other, until one begins to give way, walking backwards, still erect, pushed by his adversary. Then, perhaps by the judicious use of his tail, he recovers, prevails, and the walk commences in the opposite direction. They go at this for all they are worth, and the changes in the expression of their voices, according to the luck they are having, are remarkably plain. This performance resembles a violently aggressive fox-trot about as closely as it does anything else, and is continued until one or the other allows his tail to double under him and is bowled over, protesting loudly.

One peculiarity they have is that, when hungry, they do not fawn as most domestic animals do, but complain loudly, standing on their hind legs and grasping at the dish. If the food is withheld they scold shrilly, beating the air with their forepaws. Also, if in their work they fail in some object such as the placing of a stick, they jerk the limbs and head violently and show every sign of irritation, resuming the attempt with an impetuous violence that either makes or breaks. But as a rule they are very tractable, and after feeding will follow one all over the camp, and at times are rather a nuisance in their desire to be taken up and petted.

The male beaver has, to a certain extent, the protective instinct that dogs possess, but not of course so highly developed. I had no knowledge of this until one day I happened to be resting on my blankets on the floor after a trip — a common custom in the woods — and lying with his head on my shoulder was a six months old buck beaver. An Indian friend came in, and busied himself in some way that brought him close to my head, on the opposite side from my furry chum. Immediately the latter crossed over and stationed himself between the man's feet and my person. My friend found it necessary to pass around me, and the beaver made a quick short-cut across my face, and again took post between us. Noticing this, and thinking it might be coincidence, my companion returned to his former position, and the beaver returned also, again using my face for a runway, blowing and hissing his disapproval. It is the more remarkable in that the man was a frequent visitor, and on the best of terms with both animals, playing with them by the hour during my absence.

Another time I received a visit from a passing hunter, and on his entrance, the female beaver, always more docile than her mate, must needs go over and make an inspection of the newcomer. The male also went towards him with every sign of disapproval, and on the stranger stooping to pat the other, reached out with his hand-like forepaw, and endeavoured to pluck her away.

Beaver are far from being the dumb creatures that most animals are. While working they are continually murmuring and muttering, even if alone, and if some distance apart occasionally signal their position by short, sharp cries. It is very rarely that speaking to them does not elicit some kind of answer.

They have a large range of distinctly different sounds. The emotions of rage, sorrow, fear, joy, and contentment are expressed quite differently, and are easily recognized after a short period of observation. Often when a conversation is being carried on, they will join in with their vocal gymnastics, and the resemblance to the human voice is almost uncanny to those not accustomed to hearing it, and has been partly the cause of their undoing, as they are a very easy animal to imitate. When in trouble they whimper in a most dolorous fashion, and become altogether disconsolate. They have an imitative faculty of a sort, as any kind of bustle or quick moving around results in a like activity on their part, entailing a good deal of unnecessary gathering and pushing and dragging.

In common with most animals when tamed, beaver will answer to a name. In Canada an Irishman is known as 'a Mick', and the Indian name for beaver, Ahmik, is identical in pronunciation. So I gave them Irish names, of which the two most notable were McGinty and McGinnis, names they got to know very well, and they were suitable in more ways than one, as they both had peppery tempers, and would fight at the drop of the hat anything or anybody, regardless of size, always excepting each other or myself. My camp became known as 'The House of McGinnis', although McGinty, whimsical, mischievous as a flock of monkeys, being the female was really the boss of the place.

In the spring they become very restless, and nothing short of confinement in a wire pen will hold them. If allowed to go, they will travel far and wide; they do not forget their old home, but will return after three or four weeks, and feed all around the camp, using it as a headquarters and eventually settling in the vicinity.

I turned the two Mc's loose last spring and they made themselves a small house and a dam on a pond in a little valley back of a mountain called the Elephant, and would come when called and enter the cabin, which practice they have continued till the present time. They would always answer at intervals all the way down the lake, a not loud but very clear and penetrating sound, much like two notes of a violin sounded together, which changed to the 'hoo! hoo!' of welcome as they landed. They have ventriloquial powers, as have some other creatures in the forest country, and at times it was impossible to tell the direction from which they were coming. This no doubt is a protection against the prying ears of certain beasts with a taste for beaver meat.

Domesticated beaver will under no circumstances bite a human being, and if annoyed they will hold a finger between their dangerous teeth, exerting only just so much pressure, screeching with rage meanwhile. At a sharp exclamation they will release their hold. They are no mean adversaries in a fight, striking a series of quick raking blows with the heavy pointed claws of the front feet, and they have been known to kill dogs with one slashing bite of their razor-edged teeth, aimed always at the throat.

In the wild state they mate for life, and in captivity they show the same fidelity to the hand that reared them. They are a 'one-man dog', accepting neither food nor favour from strangers, puffing and blowing their dissatisfaction at the near approach of one they do not know; yet this little beast, with the mind of a man and the ways of a child, can work his way very deeply into the affections of those who get to know him, and I have been offered sums of money out of all proportion to their actual value, but cannot bring myself to sell them into captivity.

It is a remarkable fact the hand-raised beaver do not, to my knowledge, associate with their own kind, building for themselves within a short distance of others, but never on the same pond.

To-day I kill no more beavers, but am bent on repairing in some small measure the damage done in younger and more thoughtless days; replacing at least a part of what I have destroyed, restoring dried-out lakes to their fulness of contented families, bringing life where is nought but desolation. That I may hear in the long evenings, as in the old days, the splash of huge flat tails on the water as the working parties change shift; the queer childlike cries as they wrestle on the leaves beneath the silvery poplars that are their life, the crooning of the mothers within the lodges tending their young. That I may see the dark and gloomy forest shores shining again with Wasacsena, the brightness of newly peeled sticks, and visit and marvel over the carefully dug canals and the sand pits. And perhaps at times I may glimpse a wise old head, the head of Mishomis, the Old Man, as a pair of bright black eyes, not unfriendly, but always cautious, watch covertly my every move from out the shadows near the shore. And I shall know that I am not, after all, alone in this mighty wilderness, whilst I have for neighbours the happy colonies of Ahmik, the Beaver People.

Acknowledgements

The editor wishes to thank the authors and publishers for permission to include the following in this anthology:

Alfred A. Knopf, Inc. for "What Is Grizzly Country?" by Andy Russell from *Grizzly Country*.

Patricia Armstrong for "The Music of Nature" from the *Alberta Poetry Yearbook, 1974*.

D. P. Barnhouse for "The White Buffalo" from *Hi-Venture*, a United Church Publication.

The Book Society of Canada Limited for "The First Fire-Flowers" by John S. Morgan from *When the Morning Stars Sang Together* (1974).

The Canadian Council of Teachers of English for "Sport" by Kirk Wirsig from *Pandora's Box*.

The Canadian Publishers, McClelland and Stewart Limited, for "The Wars of the Eighties and Nineties (1882-1900)" by J. W. Chafe from *Extraordinary Tales from Manitoba History*. For "On Highway 16, Jasper" by Sid Marty from *Headwaters*. For "Picketing Supermarkets" by Tom Wayman from *Waiting for Wayman*.

Copp Clark Pitman for "Wild Horses" by Myra A. I. Smith from *All Sails Set*. Anyone knowing the address of Myra A. I. Smith is asked to contact Copp Clark Pitman, 517 Wellington St. W., Toronto, Ontario, M5V 1G1.

Denise Fair for "Buchart Gardens"

Theresa Ford for "A Tour of the Alberta Game Farm with Al Oeming".

Ivor Foster for "The Encounter".

Gage Publishing Limited for "White Cloud" by G. L. Carefoot from *Rubaboo 4*, W. J. Gage Ltd. (1965). For "Skipper for Keeps" by D. P. Barnhouse from *Rubaboo 2*, W. J. Gage Ltd. (1963). For "A Message" by Patricia Vickery from *Rubaboo 3*, W. J. Gage Ltd. (1964).

Marg Gilkes for "Barra Lad's Fabulous Leap" reprinted from *Reader's Digest*, (October 1978).

John Patrick Gillese for "Trumpets Over the Northland" from *The Rotarian*. For "Farewell, Little Flying Squirrel" from *Family Digest*.

Dana Gorbahn for "The Sun" from *A Leaf at a Time*.

Mary Simpson Hallock for "Out on the Deep Soft Snow" by James Simpson.

C. K. Harris for "Imagine the Buffalo".

Hodder & Stoughton for "Cattle Thief", for "The Wolf" and for "Fire-Flowers" by E. Pauline Johnson from *Flint and Feather*.

House of Anansi Press Limited for "The Hunters of the Deer" by Dale Zieroth.

Hurtig Publishers for "The Ruffs and the Hootles" by Mervyn J. Huston from *The Great Canadian Lover*.

Bruce Hutchison for "Death of a Giant".

Ann Lazechko for "The Acrobat".

Little, Brown & Co. (Canada) Ltd. for "Search by Air" from *The Valley of the Vanishing Birds* by Max Braithwaite.

Macmillan Company of Canada Ltd. for "The House of McGinnis" by Grey Owl from *Men of the Last Frontier*. For "The Big Fir" by Roderick Haig-Brown from *Our Heritage*. For "The Tree" by Grey Owl.

McGraw-Hill Ryerson Limited for "Sweet Grass: First Western Conservationist" by Grant MacEwan from *Portraits from the Plains* (1971).

Lorraine Meaker for "Caught Up in Colors".

Bill Meilen for "Alberta Memories" from *Heritage*.

Methuen Publications for "For Joe MacKinaw" by Jim Dumont from *Listen*.

Muriel Millen for "For a Salish Chief" from the *Spirit of Canada*.

Farley Mowat Ltd. for "The Last Husky".

Al Oeming for "Neither Voice Nor Vote".

Gordon Pellerin for "The Decision".

Mrs. Laura Rashley for "Contrast" by R. E. Rashley from *Voyageur and Other Poems*.

Rhonda Richter for "Progress" from *Reflections of Moments*.

Mildred J. R. Smith for "Ecology" from the *Alberta Poetry Yearbook, 1971*.

Andrew Suknaski for "Deathlocks" from *Leaving*, printed with permission of Repository Press.

Summerthought Ltd. for "It Began" by Jon Whyte from *Three: Noble, Thompson & Whyte*.

Talon Books Ltd. for "goshawk" by Gary Geddes from *Snakeroot* (1973).

Bill Vernon-Wood for "The Guide Knows Everything" by N. Vernon-Wood from *The National Sportsman* (June 1969).

William Collins Sons & Co. Canada Ltd. for "Let Them Eat Sawdust" by Roderick Haig-Brown from *Measure of the Year*.

Kerry Wood for "Red Man's Remedies".

Phyllis K. Young for "The Plowing" by Delbert A. Young from *Chinook Arch*.

The Young Naturalist Foundation for "Grizzly Boy" by Nancy Cooper from *Owl* (March 1978).

Since the first printing of this anthology, we have been granted permission to reprint the following copyrighted material:

"Still Shots Echo" by Ken Belford

While every effort has been made to trace the owners of copyrighted material and to make due acknowledgement, we regret having been unsuccessful with the following selections:

"Food from the Flora" by Bradford Angier
"The Owl" by Mark Bailey
"Who Wrote upon the Rocks?" by Alice A. Campbell
"This Is My Bear" by James Oliver Curwood
"The Black Stallion and the Red Mare" by Gladys Francis Lewis
"The Intruders" by Phyllis Gertrude Rodd
"The Bear at Camp" by Beatrice C. Rowley
"The Forest Fire" by Bertrand Sinclair
"The Alders" by Peter Trower